The WellBeauty

by
Heyyoung Kim
Dr. Robert Kim, MD

THE
WELL BEAUTY

A guide to your beauty tool
when skincare products don't work

Heyyoung Kim
Dr. Robert Kim, MD

DISCLAIMER

The information contained cannot be considered a substitute for treatment as prescribed by a therapist or other professional. By reading this book, you are assuming all risks associated with using the advice, data, and suggestions given below, with a full understanding that you, solely, are responsible for anything that may occur as a result of putting this information into action in any way – regardless of your interpretation of the advice.

ABOUT THE AUTHOR

H eyyoung has over 35 years of experience and has run her own brand, Respekt, since 2015. She holds degrees from Ewha Woman's University and is happily married to the love of her life. Apart from her two children, Heyyoung enjoys taking walks and meditating to reduce the stress in her life and rediscover new feelings. She believes in listening to those around her, their feelings and thoughts, and that everyday life matters in how we approach our problems.

Find more about Heyyoung @ www.respekt.co

Dr. Robert Kim was born in Seoul, South Korea. After attending medical school, he was promoted to running a skincare clinic in the heart of Seoul, where he treated many Korean celebrities. Robert has built an impressive resume as a hospital director at UrbanHeal Clinic. He is a member of the US Aesthetic Medical Society, US Anti-aging Medical Society, and the Korean Cosmetic Surgery Society. He runs his own Youtube channel and continues using cutting edge technologies combined with a natural world approach to improving the quality of skincare in all of his clients.

A man of many talents, Robert is an avid athlete, from swimming and golfing, to hiking and walking his dog. He is the drummer in a local band and sometimes vocalist with an unmatchable energy. Happiness for Robert comes from seeing other regain and restore their self-esteem and confidence after their procedures. A total professional, he has dedicated his life to improve the lives of others through a holistic approach to total wellness.

Find more about Robert @ www.urbanheal.co.kr

TABLE OF CONTENTS

PROLOGUE

"Happy girls are the prettiest."
Audrey Hepburn

Everyone is born beautiful. It is the individuality and uniqueness of each being. In beauty, there is no such thing as inferiority and superiority. It presupposes that everyone is beautiful the way they are. Thus, it is inappropriate to compare your beauty with another person. When in doubt, remember that the world holds as much beauty as the stars in the universe and as the number of people on the Earth.

Beauty is capable of healing, inspiring, and connecting us to people around us. But this is only a reality when you learn to respect and nurture your beauty. Unfortunately, a lot of people do not appreciate and respect the beauty they possess. It is disheartening that people who are not aware of the damage that negligence brings as a result of ignorance are enormous.

Do you know that beauty has the ability to help you stay alive internally and externally? But, when you fail to respect beauty, you experience doubt and alienate yourself from the rest of the world. Beauty is not all about external features and attributes. It must begin from within and then usher in the ray of hope and positivity for everyone around you to behold.

The beauty industry is a force to reckon with all over the world. It is similar to an industry where magic and fairy tales take place. The only thing that makes this far-fetched is the feeling of not being enough and the inability to see the beauty that dwells within you.

The purpose of this book is to give you a true definition of beauty that does not only revolve around external features. This book will guide you to understand how to care for your skin and solve skincare problems using the right tips. Of course, I know you have heard and read several articles and books about skincare.

But this book is structured to feed you with real-life
experiences and my encounter with various
individuals on my skincare journey.

PART ONE

THE WELLBEAUTY

"Beauty is health. Health is beauty."
André Leon Talley

I feel the need to reiterate that beauty is not entirely about physical attributes. It has so much to do with the general wellbeing of the body. When you are healthy, you are beautiful. It is only in the presence of a disease-free body that you will find it easy to do everything that concerns you. It is erroneous to pursue beauty when your wellness is at stake. Therefore, if you are using the best ingredients for your skin and have a perfect dermatologist that responds to your skin problems, you can still have a dull face or breakouts if you do not take proper care of your general wellbeing.

WellBeauty In Its Entirety

WellBeauty is beauty and wellness is combined. Simply put, it is beauty built on the premise of wellness. It is prioritizing optimal state of mind and body to bring out our best body. It means checking your overall wellbeing and getting rid of stress on your face and letting the inner wellness show for your best look.

Now that you are aware that wellness is the general wellbeing of your body. You may wonder about the different ways of making this a reality. Well, there are different ways of relieving stress from your body and improve wellbeing for your body. Without a doubt, stress is unavoidable in our daily lives. In one form or the body, you encounter stress in your activities. This stress is capable of crippling you on the inside and manifests in various forms of your appearance. For this reason, before we discuss beauty in its entire form, we must address stress and how to get rid of it from affecting our beauty.

When you encounter stress, no product works for your skin. It means that even if you go to the store and purchase the most expensive moisturizer or cream for your skin, you may not get the right result because of your stress level. Your skin glow can only become realized when you tackle stress and keep it at bay. WellBeauty is all about discovering a deeper connection between mind and body and solving the effect of stress on your beauty.

WellBeauty is a topic that addresses the root cause of your problem. The WellBeauty is a conccpt that reaches deep into your source of life and being and approaches beauty from the root cause. WellBeauty is coined from two separate words, "Well" and "Beauty." This concept is essential in understanding the concept of how health interacts with physical beauty.

From time immemorial, there has been a strong connection between the mind and body. This is why it is evident in our daily conversation and interaction.

"I've been stressed a lot these days, and look at my face, it looks awful!"

"I look ten years older after this messy situation."

"You look pale. Is everything OK?"

"The glow when you are in love.

The exemplary conversations show that we are aware that what affects our skin is not just our products but daily activities as well. Stress affects 30% of our skin condition but the skincare industry focuses on surface solutions with skincare products. The emotional, physical and mental stress that we encounter is not just affecting our minds. It also affects the way the skin looks. Everyone is aware of this truth but still looking for answers where there is none. It is the perfect explanation for people who still use of topical creams for their skin even when they are aware that there is no solution from such products.

What you may not be aware of is that your skincare problems are your responsibility. Several efforts have been put in place by the beauty industry to proffer an ideal solution for skincare problems. Ironically, thousands of years that have been put in place by the skincare industry to get the right product have not yielded the desired result. Some of the skincare products that seem to solve skin concerns and enable personal beauty are controversial in terms of efficacy and ingredient safety. Many skincare products on the shelf state that toxic or harmful ingredients are not present in these products. How true is this information? This is one of the major reasons beauty enthusiasts fall victim to the use of many harmful substances in beauty products

Things would be a lot easier if the beauty industry respects consumers. But, with the way the market looks, consumers are left with the responsibility of finding the right solution and products for their skincare problems. This desire prompts the need to find the correlation between "Wellness" and "Beauty."

The beauty industry marketing strategy only encourages product marketing without any care about the user of these products. Sadly, we lack wellness in our present beauty options. Now, you may rightly ask, "Is there anything that the beauty industry can do for a change? Don't we need more voices of holistic skincare coming from the industry, which is heard, and which is practiced easier?" These questions are essential as they will aid a simple understanding of the role of the beauty industry.

The industry is aware of this development, and certain movements are already in place to make things easier for beauty consumers. Some of these movements are evident in yoga, lifestyle, psychodermatology and other areas of medicine and entertainment.

With this information, now you know that wellness as a topic is as old as man. However, nothing concrete is done to ensure that this topic yields the much-needed result. So, I decided to pursue this knowledge not only from the beauty industry standard but in the natural form that will aid understanding. In this way, I will provide practical realistic tools and ways.

The societal perception of beauty also restricts adequate understanding of the subject matter. We still live in a world that perceives beauty as vain and superficial rather than the core of the person. Are you aware that beauty and appearance can constitute mental and psychological problems? If this issue is not well-addressed, it can lead to huge damage to not only the life of an individual but society at large. It is why beauty is better discussed when it is in the wellness-based perspective and its relationship to stress. It is so because stress revolves around our self-acceptance, self-esteem, and for our wellness in many areas.

Beauty cannot radiate without wellness, and wellness accompanies beauty. It is a virtuous cycle. We agree that only beauty on the market cannot be the solution to all our skincare problems. So, it is time to regain our understanding of the concept "WellBeauty." I believe that true beauty is wholeness. Visible beauty is multidimensional and not only on flawless skin and a likable appearance. Beauty is most compatible with practicing meditation and meditation to look into the parts that will make the beauty stand out. To achieve the right type of beauty we desire, we have to recognize what we eat, how we spend time and what happens inside us.

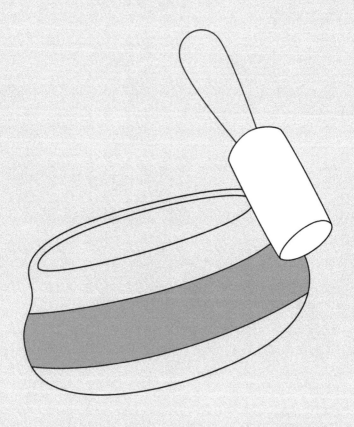

*"Beauty cannot radiate without wellness,
and wellness accompanies beauty."*

I support laying my hands on good products and cosmetics available on the market if it suits your financial budget. It is why I have a philosophical quote that guides me towards making the right choice.

Beauty Meditation

Meditation is an act of seeking clarity and calmness of mind by being aware and attentive. Meditation dates as far back as 2,600 years ago, but the evidence of meditation is as old as 5,000 years. There are many benefits of meditation including improving memory and sleep, nurturing mindfulness, compassion, slowing the aging process, relieving PMS, and even weight control.

Beauty meditation is to reach out to the deepest part of my roots and discover my individualism. Everyone has a genetic part of their look, and this is the mystery that surrounds our beauty. In addition to my skincare routine, I make it a habit to indulge in meditation. My beauty meditation helps me to manage my stressful life and my skin reveals what is going on inside of me. Practicing beauty meditation is a good way to discover our true beauty and connection between mind and skin.

Meditation is beneficial in so many ways. First, it can improve your skin by physically supplying fresh oxygen to your skin. Secondly, it helps to normalize the blood flow and allows a balanced perspective and appreciation of beauty. Meditation can also be practically incorporated into your pursuit and make your beauty routine a mindful experience. The good news is that when you are more mindful and intentional, it becomes evident in the results your skin produces.

Although there are several benefits of meditation, it saddens me to discover that many people do not truly appreciate the goodness of meditation. Strangely, only the invisible benefits of meditation are present but the benefits on the skin appearance are ignored. For this reason, I encourage all my clients to incorporate meditation into their beauty routine to produce quicker results.

When you are stressed and preoccupied with certain emotions, people can catch it. When you are under stress, worried, tense, you know it all shows. On the contrary, when you are in love or excited, your complexion displays it. Your skin delivers what's inside. It shows some things going on inside. Your skin operates as an indicator. It shows the weather in your mood. Many parts of my skin problems and visible characteristics (attitude, posture, puffiness, dryness, acne, dullness, lack of liveliness, the sparkle in my eyes etc) influenced by the stress and tension I held even without knowing but meditation or helped me throughout my whole life.

Among all the benefits of meditation, one thing I witnessed when I engaged in my meditative practices was that my skin glowed and changed drastically. My beauty affirmation helped me restore my confidence and helped me enjoy all the benefits of my beauty. What meditation did to my skin is so powerful and intense that I have learned to only see the only benefit meditation brings to my beauty.

I started my meditation for so many reasons and benefits such as stress reduction, improving my focus, calming my emotions and reflecting on myself. And the actual benefits kept me meditating for more than 30 years and still my go-to life savior. Regardless of the benefits you derive from mediation, it would be good if you change your mindset and see mediation as an essential ingredient for beauty purposes.

Breathing for your beauty is practical, and you just need a moment wherever you are; nothing else needed. Breathe away your tension and stress, breathe in and feel the essence of your beauty, your unique beautiful being. If you are already a meditator and familiar with the meditation techniques, try your next focusing on your beauty purpose. In beauty meditation, the point is you do meditation for beauty purposes.

Being beautiful and staying beautiful are two different things. It presupposes that you are beautiful but may not be able to maintain your beauty because of ignorance. However, beauty mediation revolves around helping you discover your true identity and appreciate it. There are stress hormones in the body that are responsible for all the acne and dull skin you suffer. There are lots of beauty tips that will guarantee you a good skincare routine. But a good way to get started is to make use of our **RESPEKT Beauty Meditation app**.

Want Stress-Free Skin? Use RESPEKT Beauty Meditation App.

Information is available at your disposal on how to care for your skin. But a good way to get all the information you need is to use our RESPEKT Beauty Meditation app. All you need to do is to follow the simple steps and enjoy all the benefits of a meditation app.

To get the best use of this app, follow these simple steps:

- Begin by taking a deep breath in and hold it for a few seconds. As you exhale, you say to yourself 'Relax now'. Repeat two more times.

- When you relax, the beauty within your skin can fully emerge.

- Now, repeat these words.

  "Each day and every day, I get better and better.

  My skin is beautiful because I care deeply for it.

  When I ruminate on my negativities, they affect my facial expressions, bring about wrinkles and reduce my happy glow.

  I am relaxing my mind and body. By doing so, relaxing my facial expressions, letting wrinkles melt away. This allows me to smile more and frown less, making my gorgeous skin radiate."

This practice will help you start a new and positive thought process that will help your natural beauty flourish. So, if you want your skin to be at their best, learn to freshen up at all times and relieve the tension that is inside of you.

Meditation As A Skincare Solution

Before feeling frustrated over your skin issues or blaming age for your skin problem, you must look into wellness and see how it contributes to your skin glow. After discovering the cause of your skin problems, it is important to make conscious efforts into meditative practices as a skincare solution.

Health Benefits Of Meditation

Meditation reduces negative energy: Research examining meditative practices has revealed that medication is a good way to reduce negative energies such as stress, fear, worry, and anxiety. Various techniques such as relaxation sessions and meditation have real benefits for people suffering from skin conditions like psoriasis, eczema, acne and vitiligo (a pigment disorder).

Meditation slows down the aging process: Meditating for just a few minutes every day brings energy (also known as prana) into your body and creates a feeling of calm and relaxation. During meditation, prana helps repair your body's tissues and cells which give skin a fresh, youthful glow.

Also, mindful breathing while meditating adds oxygen to the skin, which is necessary in boosting cellular health. This increased oxygen rejuvenates your skin, balancing your body and your mind while transforming your body's cells and tissues. It improves your complexion, reduces wrinkles and slows down the aging process from the inside out. Meditation also lowers blood pressure and tension-related pain such as headaches, ulcers, insomnia, muscle aches and joint problems, making you look and feel younger.

Meditation improves self-confidence and mood: Your complexion connects to feelings of self-confidence. When your skin looks better, your sense of confidence increases. A regular meditation practice increases the brain's ability to repair itself and grow new neural connections. Like a muscle, these neural pathways get stronger and more effective over time with practice.

As a result, people who meditate experience more happiness, inner peace, and an overall sense of wellbeing. Meditation also increases your brain's serotonin production, which makes you feel better and improves your mood. Like a candle, meditation shines your light. And the more you meditate, the more you glow. Indeed, happiness comes from the inside out.

Meditation helps you make healthier choices: With meditation practice comes more awareness of your breath, your body, and your surroundings. It leads to increased ability to pause, be present and consider your lifestyle choices. It can manifest in several ways, from communicating more effectively with your loved ones or simply becoming more conscious of where and how your food, clothes or skincare products are made.

Meditation can also create a gentle space to slow down and enjoy the process of taking care of yourself, such as taking a few extra minutes to enjoy taking care of your skin. When we are more in touch with the present moment, we can fully exist and feel gratitude for every moment in our lives – the only moment we ever truly have.

Myths About Meditation

There are so many myths and misconceptions that surround meditation. These myths that surround meditation make it difficult for a lot of people to comprehend what meditation means. This misconception deprives people of reaping the benefit associated with meditation. Some common myths that surround meditation are:

1. Meditation is difficult to practice.

Meditation being difficult to practice is by far the biggest myth that most people believe. The reason is meditation has its roots in eastern philosophy. Although mediation can function as a practice for religious purposes, it does not make it difficult to practice. Meditation in its current format has a heavy secular-leaning and is a lot of fun to undertake. The techniques are dis-entangled from the trappings of any religion and focus on simple inhaling and exhaling of your breath.

2. There is only one form of meditation.

I do not know where this myth originated from, but it is a popular belief amongst several people. The most common image that one conjures up upon meditation is a person sitting in a crossed-legged lotus position.

"*Practicing beauty meditation is a good way to discover our true beauty and connection between mind and skin.*"

The reality, however, is that meditation comes in all imaginable shapes and sizes, and only a few fit this typical imaginary. Meditation is visualization; it focuses on gentle, meditative movements, it is chanting of mantras and finally, it is using mindfulness in everyday activities like dishwashing or eating.

3. A quiet mind is a prerequisite for a successful meditation.

Many believe that meditation is about preventing the flow of our thoughts or vacating our mind of them. We can't control our thoughts and emotions, but we can control how we allow them to affect our wellbeing. Meditation is not about enforcing silence on our thoughts but finding a quiet corner that already exists among all these thoughts.

4. It takes years to get any benefit from meditation.

This myth is ridiculous and nowhere close to the truth. Meditation has both long-term and short-term benefits. Studies have established that even first-timers experience the benefits of meditation within just weeks of practicing a wide range of physical, emotional, and psychological advantages. From sleeping like a baby to a strengthened immune system and sharper focus are some of the commonplace benefits for the newbies in the world of meditation.

5. Meditation is a stress and pain management tool.

This is the biggest myth perpetuated in the west. Yes, meditative practices have immense therapeutic value hence are used as an effective tool for pain and stress management. However, the chief purpose of any meditative practice is to delve deeper into the meaning of life. It is the very core neglected and studies focus only on the health benefits. Health is but one of the many benefits.

The true understanding of meditation would come only when you understand the basic premise of it. Should you treat meditation singularly from the lens of health, you would remain in the periphery of what meditation has to offer to you.

Meditation is for anyone and everyone, and it's a treasure trove of benefits! Now that we have busted some common myths about meditation for you, the world of serenity and tranquility awaits you.

Skin Benefits Of Meditation

Most of us are probably familiar with the mental health benefits of meditation, but did you know that meditation can improve the condition of your skin as I have mentioned before.

It All Shows in Your Face: Skin is our largest organ, and it can be a surprisingly good indicator of issues that are going on inside your body and brain. Blushing is the prime example of just how revealing your skin can be when it comes to emotions. If a signal from your brain can change your skin's color in mere seconds, can you imagine just how powerful your mind is? How much can you change with daily meditation?

It improves skin conditions: Skin issues can be hard to deal with and can take a toll on your mental state and can be incredibly stressful in and of itself. Of course, there are skin conditions that improve by rigorous skincare or medication, but for many of them, you might only need to give yourself a break and try your best to relax. Dermatologists who study deeply in the brain and body connections use traditional medicine and also recommend meditation and relaxation techniques to their patients to treat their symptoms.

Meditative Practices

A. MINDFULNESS and MBSR: Integral Part of Holistic Wellness

What is this life if, full of care?

We have no time to stand and stare.

The above lines from Williams Henry Davies poem are a perfect illustration of the constant running around of humans in a bid to meet certain expectations. The desire to meet these expectations makes us oblivious to the happy moments that stare us right at the face.

The history of mindfulness as a practice used as a skincare routine dates back to ancient times. The history of mindfulness and the current form of Mindfulness-Based Stress Reduction (MBSR) is fascinating.

- **What is Mindfulness?**

Just as the name suggests, mindfulness is a practice in which the mind is 100% in the present moment. It implies that whatever activity you get involved with, your mind is present with you. You are inseparable from the contents of your mind. But, when your mind cannot fathom the happenings or situations around you, it leads to anxiety and despair.

Mindfulness is the innate ability of the human mind to attend to all the tasks at hand. In the state of mindfulness, you do not worry about the past or future. Instead, you are concerned with the present. Focus on the present moment comes with training and practice. Breathing methods and guided imagery, among others are an integral part of training your mind to be stable and focused.

- **How the theory of mindfulness began**

Contrary to what people believe, mindfulness is not a product of the western world but the prominent Buddhism. The concept of mindfulness originated from the Pali word *sati*, which translates into attention, awareness, consciousness. Several people think that Buddhism is the only religion where mindfulness is present. But this is far from the truth as Japanese Zen and Hinduism also practice the act of mindfulness.

Now, the right question to ask is how the practice of mindfulness began in the Western world. Jon-Kabat Zinn introduced the theory of mindfulness to western society. He was influenced by the teachings of Philip Kapleau, a Zen missionary when he was a student. Absorbed in his teachings,

Jon-Kabat Zinn decided to pursue further studies on the subject matter under the tutelage of Thích Nhất Hạnh.

- **What is Mindfulness-Based Stress Reduction (MBSR)?**

Jon-Kabat Zinn, in a bid to fit the theory of mindfulness to suit western world extricated all connotations of religion and spiritual practices of the theory. Therefore, in 1979, he introduced the concept of mindfulness-based stress reduction to Western society. This practice is influential and has revolutionized the concept of stress-free living.

MBSR is an eight-week formal training that encourages the use of variety of techniques that includes yoga, body awareness, meditation, and various behavioral patterns. The singular aim of the MBSR program is to get rid of all forms of stress that are detrimental to the general wellbeing of your body and help you stay healthy in all aspects of life. Interestingly, mindfulness is not just any scientific concept that possesses spiritual roots. Rather, it is an invaluable lesson that will help you live your life accordingly. It is so because the only way to live life is to be fully conscious of everything that concerns your existence.

B. RAIN Meditative practice

Look around you, and there are lots of emotions flying around. Everything from billboards, flying and even magazines exaggerate the concept of happiness. These platforms make it seem like the only emotion present in the world is happiness. Being happy and putting your best foot forward in the most adverse circumstances has become the new mantra.

Most importantly, there is always a need to be happy regardless of the situations that surround you. As a rule, the best way to suppress any form of negative emotion that threatens to consume you is to stay happy and find reasons to be happy. You do not need to live in denial of any form as this may make it very difficult for you to be truly happy. Whenever you refuse to accept the reality of your emotions, you deny yourself the opportunity to be in touch with your true emotion, and this is disastrous for your health.

The spiritual world, particularly on the eastern side of the globe, gives supreme importance to self-awareness and tackling conflict through cultivating the inner balance of mind, body, and emotions. There are various techniques and formats for getting this balance right.

RAIN is an acronym for a four-step process- Recognize, Allow, Investigate, and Natural awareness. It is a concept that is significant for practicing mindfulness. In this practice, you learn to accept everything about your environment- good and bad- with no thoughts of judgment.

RAIN meditation aim is to walk you through all your stress and confusion which hang above your mind clouding your perception. These four steps strengthen our mind and our ability to accept ourselves without the harness of criticism and self-blame.

What is the history of RAIN?

Like most meditative practices and techniques, RAIN too has its genesis in the eastern Buddhist philosophy. RAIN was conceptualized approximately a decade back by a handful of Buddhist teachers as a mindfulness tool to sort out a range of difficult feelings.

The credit for creating and popularizing RAIN in the west goes to Michele McDonald of Insight Meditation Society RAIN is of immense help by our understanding and sifting through emotions that bring suffering to us.

- **How to deconstruct the concept?**

  Let us digest the acronym RAIN and understand what the concept represents.

  R (Recognize) - Recognize everything about you and your environment. It is the root of understanding. It is much easier for you to act when you understand your thoughts and translate these thoughts into words. The best way to go about it is to give words to your feelings when certain things are happening around you. It simply means that you must learn to use words in appreciating your thoughts. At first, it might be difficult to recognize those emotions as they take place but with practice, things get better. Remember, recognizing.

  A (Allow) – You will not be able to control everything around you. So, allow life to take its natural course. You cannot control everything around you. To make things easy, see the situations around you to be a card which you can slot into one of the three different categories: By taking our mind away from it, judging the situation, and lastly by being deadened towards the entire situation. In this way, you learn to hit the pause button in some situations and hit the acknowledgement button. Just because we acknowledged our negative feelings doesn't mean we agree with them. Don't confuse acknowledgment with agreement.

I *(Investigate):* The third step in this four-step process is Investigation. It is here that you ask yourself some probing and pertinent questions regarding your situation. These questions help you look at your situation with a lens of wisdom and help us arrive at a happy place. Starting from "Why do I feel the way I do?" and "Was my reaction beneficial?" to "What can I do to support myself?" These investigative questions encompass many areas to help you understand yourself better and create a harmonious symbiosis between your emotions and your responses. It consequently becomes a nurturing factor to have a more meaningful life.

N *(Natural- awareness):* The last step in RAIN is disassociating yourself from the negative energies. This non-identification means that our definition of who we are is not limited to a particular emotion or feeling. When this happens it paves a way for Natural loving awareness. The N in RAIN is coming back to your roots: Intuitive and open living through natural awareness.

- **How to move from theory to practice**

  It is not simple enough to know the theoretical approach of RAIN. You must be able to put all of what you have read into practice. Most importantly, you must understand that no situation is too small to use RAIN as a strategy. So, this section will help you put everything into practice. How? Just read up and follow the simple description.

Choose a quiet corner for this meditative process. Close your eyes and inhale and exhale a few breaths. Focus your mind on the situation that is responsible for extracting a difficult reaction from you. It could be anything troubling you. Got handed over a pink slip? Your partner broke up with you? Your inputs were not solicited for an important project at work? Dive into the situation in your mind and relieve the anger and the despair. And then ask yourself the questions that would help you foster a meaningful relationship with your emotions.

Skincare ritual is also a perfect time for us to apply the RAIN process and recognize your feelings and emotions and let it go. It could be a time to let go of any tension and stress and come back to your peaceful senses.

Your beauty ritual can go silently, or you can whisper the mantra to yourself. It doesn't always have to be a positive affirmation or blessings to yourself, and it can just be the words to recognize and name your emotions at the moment. Just make it into the time you serve for your wellness purpose. Any instant or customized ritual can also act as the best solution for you.

This therapeutic practice has more benefits than many people want to accept and will also provide a long-lasting effect.

Essential Meditation Technique For Beginners-Beauty Breathing

The core of beauty meditation is breathing. When you pay attention to your breathing, you become a part of the present.

Our RESPEKT Beauty Meditation app, which is available on Android, iOS and other platforms provide the simple steps that will boost your beauty.

Most importantly, you need to find a suitable place to begin your meditation to avoid any form of disturbance. These steps are easy to understand. All you need to do is to follow these directions:

- Close your eyes
- Inhale and exhale air for four seconds each
- Take another breath for four seconds and breathe out again.
- Feel the air moving in and out of your lungs.
- Take some time to observe your breathing, emotions, and how it feels.
- Take another deep breath for four seconds. But this time let your intention to breathe in fresh air that will revitalize your skin.
- Keep focusing on your breathing and know that your skin is in its tension and needs to be in a relaxation mood.
- Repeat the breathing, focusing on breathing for one minute.

- Take time to notice that you are taking the tension and stress out from the inside and free your skin to its natural state.

- Tips for Meditation technique beginners

Meditation beginners require useful tips to enable them to carry out the meditation exercises properly and avoid making a grave mistake. Some of the useful tips are:

1. *A useful tool*

The best way to start the meditation exercise is to see it as a useful and important tool for your wellbeing. The fact of the matter is that it can be incredibly useful and has the potential to change your life completely. Or rather how you perceive it. With a calmer mind and soul, you might start noticing the world around you is changing along with your internal one. Being aware, mindful, focused, stable, and calm are all positive things and meditation can be such an amazing coping mechanism and a tool that can help you achieve this state of mind.

2. *Keep it simple.*

A sweet and short meditation can be enough, especially if you're a novice and only starting your journey. The five-step journey that will aid you keep it simple as a beginner are:

- Find a calm spot, somewhere or anywhere you can be alone for a few minutes.

- Sit or lie down.

- Close your eyes and allow a natural flow of your breath.

- As you observe your breath, allow any thoughts or actions to appear as you keep your focus on your breath. Don't try to fight them. Acknowledge its presence and return to your breathing.

- Repeat the process as long as you like and then slowly return from the meditative state.

You see! It is really simple.

3. Take it easy.

There is no need to rush into it. It can be tempting to over-analyze meditation and dissect what it is, what it means, and so on. If you are a beginner I suggest you start slowly. Don't pay too much attention to all the mysticism surrounding meditation. It doesn't have to be religious. It does not have to take long hours or consist of a tedious process. Meditation can be whatever you make it. I suggest you choose a short, guided meditation and simply try it out. I am positive that there is a suitable meditation style for every single person.

4. Make it a part of your skincare routine.

I think this is one of the most useful and practical tips I could give you. Instead of doing your skincare in front of the mirror and analyzing every pore, wrinkle, and blemish, I encourage you to try doing it while you meditate. Take that precious time and allow your skin to relax and absorb all the nourishing ingredients. As you meditate and gently massage your skin, the daily stress will slowly dissipate, and you will feel grateful for your skin, body, and mind. Touch is such an underrated sense. Touch your skin, pay attention to any sensations that arise, and simply allow them to be. Your skin and mind are two peas in a pod.

They stay connected so that your skin can reflect the state of your mind.

5. *Use our RESPEKT Beauty Meditation app*

Our app is a great tool for beginners, especially those that are "skincare addicts."

There are a plethora of different meditations to choose. Combine your meditation and your skincare and nourish both at the same time.

The Ultimate Attitude- Respect

One factor that encouraged my desire to pursue wellness-rooted beauty is respect. You will agree with me that respect supersedes love. It is because respect is a vague concept when compared to love. I have witnessed so many incidents when someone loves another person but does not respect the individual. I held on to the concept of respect and it has brought me tremendous relief and result. Thus, I have learned that respect is a prerequisite for love.

Respect is above subjectivity. Respect is a tool that enables us appreciate things, and it is a guideline to realize their original meaning. Respect is important in all the choices that we make in life including things that affect us and this is applicable in the skincare industry. In skincare and beauty, it is respect that makes it easy for me to reach wellness-based beauty.

PART TWO

WELLNESS AS THE GROUND OF YOUR BEAUTY

"You don't have to tell it; it shows in the face."
Lolue Pratt Brown

Beauty is the core of a person. It distinguishes one person from the other and is most visible when we bring it out. Beauty is the barometer of our wellness, and wellness encompasses the whole human being, mind, body and soul.

Beauty is visible but beyond skin deep. Beauty philosophy is important because just like any other area of our lives, it is related to how we accept and embrace ourselves and comprehend surrounding. There is nothing subjective as beauty in the world. The standard of beauty varies from one culture to another, time, and societal expectations. It even differs from time to time within oneself. It changes depending on the situation, the emotions at the moment, age, and health status and even financial status. More than anything else beauty can be subjective as it can be. It is important to establish one's standard.

In the previous chapter, I had already stated that stress is detrimental to the skin. But, in this chapter I will take special care in emphasizing the dangers of stress and the damage it can bring to the skin.

Stress- The Invisible Enemy Of Beauty

You will agree that you find it easy to deal with your enemies when you can identify them. But how can you deal with an unseen enemy? It is the greatest challenge that concerns dealing with stress considering it are an invisible enemy.

High levels of stress hormones and related mental and emotional distress can not only exacerbate skin issues. They can even trigger a skin condition that would otherwise stay dormant. Chronic inflammation related to stress has been linked to various skin diseases and conditions, from mild acne and dermatitis to more severe issues such as psoriasis and alopecia.

Certain skin conditions can sadly cause lots of stress and emotional turmoil to the individual dealing with them. It can become a vicious circle of stress and flare-ups and stress. Luckily a lot of skin problems can be solved or at least improved by using the right skincare and leading a healthy lifestyle.

- **How does stress manifest on the skin and body?**

Flaky and dry skin: The release of cortisol decreases your body's natural ability to retain the water level. A rise in cortisol means a drop in estrogen. Less estrogen implies a less than optimal level of collagen leading to a loss in moisture in your skin. The problem becomes enormous if you are not replenishing your body by drinking water. The resultant effect, of course, will be dry, flaky and irritable skin that is internally screaming for hydration. Moreover, you wouldn't want to look papery, would you?

Face Irruptions: Acne is not just a teenage issue; it's a stress-induced issue. The release of cortisol causes the skin to flare up and break out in acne and other skin problems like psoriasis and eczema. Next time when your face breaks out, don't dismiss it just wave a hand. It's calling out for help.

Fine Lines and Wrinkles: With so many products promising to fight premature signs of aging, who knew the main culprit, is stress? Sugar levels shoot up as a result of cortisol released. The body then begins a process to combat the high sugar levels. It, unfortunately, hardens your skin and accelerates the appearance of fine lines and wrinkles.

Puffy Eyes: Eyes are perhaps the first to show the signs of stress on your face. Remember how your eyes ache, puff up and you roam around with dark circles under them after meeting a particularly tough deadline? We know it is anything but a pretty sight. Your skin goes into self-repair mode while you dream away at night. Not enough sleep causes fluid to collect under your eyes and make you look like a mess in the morning.

Grooved Nails: If you see deep horizontal ridges on your nails, it is a message that stress has compromised your body.

Skincare And Your Mind

Skincare is one of the most important factors when it comes to your skin and its health. Not only because it nourishes, moisturizes, protects, and repairs your skin, but also because using it can create a simple and relatively quick daily routine that helps you relax and enter a state of mindfulness, similar to meditation. When you make sure you are putting some effort into your appearance, you also tend to feel more confident, and in control, which can significantly reduce the stress and pressure you feel in your everyday life.

Skincare can't be used as a quick band-aid but taking care of your skin and body will work wonders or your mental wellbeing and vice versa. When you feel confident and relaxed, you are more inclined to take care of yourself and when you take care of your body as a whole, you are bound to become more mentally and emotionally balanced.

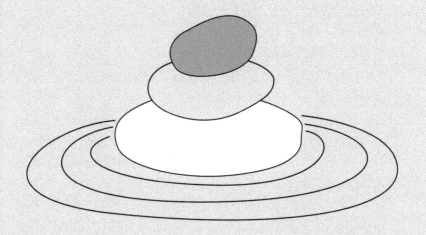

"High levels of stress hormones and related mental and emotional distress can not only exacerbate skin issues"

Skincare, meditation, exercise, and other wellness rituals and habits are a feedback loop. When you feel better, you look better. Others see you in a different light, and most importantly, you see yourself as worthy of having clear and healthy skin.

- **So, What Can You Do?**

Reducing stress is one of those things that are easier said than done; however there are simple ways to take care of your physical and mental health and regain healthy, youthful, and glowing skin in the process.

There are some obvious solutions when it comes to stress relief, such as massages and regular meals at your favorite restaurant, but small rituals can be just as beneficial and relaxing as the more expensive and extravagant self-care solutions, perhaps even more so. It truly doesn't take much to let go and relax after a long day. A few minutes of beauty meditation once or twice a day, a nourishing nighttime skincare routine, reading before bed, and even cooking a nutritious meal, can be both beneficial on a completely practical level and also help you release any anxiety and stress.

How To Manage Stress

Effective stress management is key to achieving a beautiful body (and a peaceful mind). It requires a multi-prong approach that only skincare and beauty products cannot address alone. We cannot eliminate stress from our daily activities, but we can manage it effectively. How? You are about to find out.

However, several people desire to settle for quick fixes. But quick fixes are only effective in the short run. But for a sustained effect, a holistic approach needs to be adopted. Healthy living is not just about physical health but is inclusive of mental and emotional aspects as well. But, to manage stress effectively, you need to adopt a good means of managing stress that will be effective in the long run. Some of these strategies are:

Exercise: The benefits of physical exercise are as a stress reliever. Exercising produces endorphins, a chemical that is regarded as a natural painkiller and helps you sleep soundly leading to a reduction in stress.

Eat Right: Eating the right kind of food is an effective counterbalance to your stress. Food enriched with Vitamin C, Omega-3 Fatty Acids, complex carbohydrates, and magnesium is important nutrients for stress reduction.

Mediate: Health is beyond physical health. It is a state of overall wellness. Meditation is instrumental in restoring the calm and tranquility that stress robs you. That's because during meditation, you focus all your energies on being aware of your breath, the deep inhale and the slow exhale. Slowly, the jumbled mess of thoughts in your head gets unknotted one by one. You can feel the stress leaving your body as it gives up its tense posture and is replaced by a feeling of relaxation.

Meditation gives you the platform to be aware of your innermost thoughts and regulate stress. It is a simple and cost-effective method to beat stress that everyone can do anywhere. The benefits of mediation do not end with the session ending. They remain with you throughout the day helping you deal with things calmly.

Looking good is more than using beauty products. It's about leading a stress-free mindful life and appreciating every moment you live because there is nothing like celebrating life and its bounties.

Pss-Perceived Stress Scale

Try this simple self- assessment to check on your stress at the moment and, in turn, the effects it puts on your skin. Try to incorporate beauty meditation into your beauty routine to diminish the effects of stress on your skin.

The questions in this scale ask you about your feelings and thoughts during the last month. In each case, you will ask to indicate by circling how often you felt or thought a certain way.

Answer the following assessment questions using these options:

0 = Never

1 = Almost Never

2 = Sometimes

3 = Fairly Often

4 = Very Often

INTELLECTUAL	Never	Almost Never	Some-times	Fairly Often	Very Often
1. How often have you been upset because of something that happened unexpectedly?	0	1	2	3	4
2. Have you felt that you were unable to control the important things in your life?	0	1	2	3	4
3. How often have you felt nervous and "stressed"?	0	1	2	3	4
4. How often have you felt confident about your ability to handle your problems?	0	1	2	3	4
5. Have you felt that things were going your way?	0	1	2	3	4
6. How often have you found that you could not cope with all the things you had to do?	0	1	2	3	4
7. How often have you been able to control irritations in your life?.	0	1	2	3	4
8. How often have you felt that you were on top of things?	0	1	2	3	4
9. How often have you been angered because of things that were outside of your control?.	0	1	2	3	4
10. How often have you felt difficulties were piling up so high that you could not overcome them?	0	1	2	3	4
TOTAL					

Cohen, S., Kamarck, T., and Mermelstein, R. (1983) mentions that it is easy to determine your PSS score by following these directions:

First, reverse your scores for questions 4, 5, 7, and 8. On these 4 questions, change the scores like this:

0 = 4,	3 = 1,
1 = 3,	4 = 0.
2 = 2,	

Now add up your scores for each item to get a total. My total score is _____.Individual scores on the PSS can range from 0 to 40, with higher scores indicating higher perceived stress.

▶ Scores ranging from 0-13 would be considered low stress.

▶ Scores ranging from 14-26 would be considered moderate stress.

▶ Scores ranging from 27-40 would be considered high perceived stress. Disclaimer: The scores on the following self-assessment do not reflect any particular diagnosis or course of treatment. They are a tool to help assess your level of stress.

The Perceived Stress Scale (PSS) is the most widely used psychological instrument for measuring the perception of stress.

My Beauty Philosophy- No Harsh Chemicals, No Stress

From the age of 12, I paid keen attention to my skincare routine, but I failed to realize that the chemicals brought much damage to the skin. I remember I received skincare cosmetics set with a beautiful formula. It had colorful packaging and a lovely fragrance. I was excited to have my own set of skincare treatment set. So, I carefully washed my face and put it in the 3-step skincare routine set which was in those adorable bottles.

I went to bed in the hopes of waking up to a beautiful and flawless face, but I got the direct opposite of what I desired. My skin was pink and reddish with the trace of scratches that seemed to be what I had one to calm my itchy skin. Not only that, one big reason I can't forget that cosmetic set was that it was the day my acne started for the next seven years. It was a historical incident that had led me to think about the cleanliness, gentleness of skincare ingredients and the danger of harmful/ irritating ingredients for the first time.

The next day, I paid a visit to a dermatologist who emphasized the word 'respect.' His exact words were "Only if they made the lotion with respect for the users..." These words were imprinted on my heart and made me recognize that the one thing our skin and beauty deserve was 'respect.'

It was not just avoiding the use of products that had chemicals; I paid close attention to my mother's words, "You need to take a break, breathe out your worries and stress, look into your mind because it shows in your face." Her words were a reminder of the dangers of stress on the skin because as a psychologist and meditator for more than 50 years and she knew how dangerous stress was.

In my early years in Korea, I learned to do mindful breathing. Whenever I encountered life's big and small problems or insecurities, my mother led me to deep breathing. By doing this, my problems became manageable, my heart regained the calm normal rhythm of its own and my tense muscles relaxed. Not only the signs of my heightened emotions did find peace but my flushed appearance in the mirror subsided. I could smile from my heart again.

I found myself applying meditation techniques in whatever I do, when I study, working on my projects, or other chores. I learned to mindfully breathe and watch all my thoughts and emotions rise and disappear like the clouds in the sky, learned to allow and accept them and protect myself in it. I discovered after a long time that it had a huge impact not only on the inside but on the outside as well. I didn't even notice it, but I was incorporating it in the skincare routine that I breathe, visualize and make it into a ritual. My skincare routine became the time to be present at the moment, face myself and more pleasantly engaged in it.

Growing up in Korea, I was always too lazy to do a skincare routine. At the time, K-beauty 10 steps skincare was worshipped and a popular cosmetics product. There were lots of amazing stories about the product and the wonder it worked. I was hopeful that I would get the same results. Unfortunately, it wasn't for me. The mindfulness of skincare let me enjoy the short moment of the routine and motivated me to do it every day with a sense of self-care.

My first unpleasant experience using the skincare set was very visible at an early age. Thus, when I was pregnant, I suffered greatly from it. My face was red and bumpy because of the effects of hormones. I got stressed every time, and I became the witness of the vicious cycle of stress, depression and skin problems. At this point I remembered the effects of meditation and it got the calmness of my mind back.

Someone may not have told you, but you don't need a lot of money or time for wellness and beauty. It has to be sustainable. To be sustainable it has to be skin-friendly and simple. In that sense we are lucky that we have various options in the market, and we have meditation. In choosing a skincare product or routine, you must be careful to respect your skin and only feed it with what is best for it.

You may not have been doing things the right way, and now you are skeptical about the choices you have made and how they affect your skin. But, not to worry, it is never too late to start a skincare routine.

So, I have stuck to my beauty philosophy of no chemicals, no stress. Trust me; this has never been wrong!

Beauty Philosophy Of Celebrities And Women

The female gender is naturally concerned about beauty and how it makes them feel. It is why it is not strange to see female celebrities and women in the world creating beauty philosophies that suit them. Beautiful skin requires commitment not miracles. What makes you different makes you beautiful. Admire someone else's beauty without questioning your own.

An excerpt from Nora Ephron, *I feel bad about my neck* states, "One of my biggest regrets...is that I didn't spend my youth staring lovingly at my neck. It never crossed my mind to be grateful for it. It never crossed my mind that I would be nostalgic about a part of my body that I took for granted. Of course it's true that now that I'm older, I'm wise and sage and mellow. And it's also true that I honestly do understand just what matters in life. But guess what? It's my neck."

Another celebrity Kate Winslet, from Net-a-Porter magazine, expresses her beauty philosophy in this quote "I'm baffled that anyone might not think women get more beautiful as they get older. Confidence comes with age and looking beautiful comes from the confidence someone has in themselves."

Geena Gocero states that "When a person has gone through the journey of finding and pursuing their most authentic self and shares that gift, for me, that's beautiful."

Raise Your Beauty Awareness.

There is a lot of emphasis on beauty as it affects a certain part of the body without due consideration to the beauty within. This is saddening especially as it sends the wrong message and information to beauty enthusiasts. Here is the good news! You are in charge of your beauty. Well, I am not surprised if you do not understand this. But the remaining part of this book will provide further insight.

- **Beauty Mantra**

It is a simple example of Beauty Mantra Meditation. Follow the steps anytime, anywhere. You can find full, guided beauty meditation on our RESPEKT Beauty Meditation app.

Find a quiet place where you won't be disturbed for about 2minutes.

Remember the fact that your wellness will show on your skin.

- Focus on yourself, your eyes, your face, and your whole being.

- In front of a mirror, look into your eyes. If a mirror is not available, close your eyes and picture the most beautiful self.

- Find a statement you needed or want to hear, the word that you would say to the one you love the most.

- "I love and appreciate my body and everything it enables me to do. "

- Repeat it silently or aloud, over and over with your breath.

- Take 20 seconds to reflect and try to internalize this affirmation.

- End this mantra meditation with a gentle smile.

Your Wellness, Your Beauty- 8 Dimensions Of Wellness

Wellness is a broad concept that means being healthy in all dimensions of our lives. Sometimes, we worry about various things that are not necessary. These anxieties and worries make it very difficult for us to experience joy and get the fulfillment of health that we deserve.

It is why it is important to create a balance in our lives so that we do not succumb to activities and circumstances that will affect our health negatively. Building good relationships makes it easier for us to measure balance and stay in control at all times. However, the only way to achieve this balance is to feel good about ourselves by promoting good habits and routines.

Good practices are also an important part of maintaining wellness. Positive habits lead to physical, emotional, social, spiritual, and all-around wellness. To properly understand wellness, we need to look into the eight dimensions of wellness and how it affects your wellbeing. SAMHSA (Substance Abuse and Mental Health Services Administration) numerates some of these eight dimensions of wellness as emotional, spiritual, social, occupational, financial, environmental, physical and intellectual wellness.

- **Emotional wellness**

Over the years, beauty trends have changed drastically. Every era brings a new more innovative trend either marked by a feature or a product. The beauty industry throughout its evolution has neglected emotional wellness as a key factor in determining a person's overall health as well as the health of their skin.

The present trend gives emotional wellness the credit it deserves. Experts nowadays emphasize how huge of an impact emotional wellness can have on beauty or the other way around. The modern-day consumer wants to achieve beauty that makes them feel good. The trend is shifting to acknowledge how one's emotional state can impact one skin or vice versa.

So what is the connection?

If you are wondering what emotional wellness has to do with beauty, we will attempt to form a simple connection for you. Ever experienced a pimple popping up when you worry about something? That's your emotional state affecting your skin. The mind is worried, and your skin reacts to it. Some other examples are the skin looking dull when you are feeling depressed or the appearance of dark circles because you've had a difficult few days.

Moving on to how our beauty can affect our emotional wellness, well, there's a very simple explanation for this. Ever felt low because of the way you look? The condition of your skin or how you look directly affects your mood and confidence. A bad hair day can very well ruin your self-esteem (Although we really shouldn't make beauty a standard for happiness).

We have all felt uncertain of ourselves because of our acne, dark circles, or facial hair. People who struggle with cystic acne or other skin conditions feel very depressed because of their skin and this leads to self-doubt. Another aspect is how pursuing beauty makes us happy like doing skincare or makeup.

How to achieve emotional wellness

Now that we have established how strong the correlation between emotional wellness and beauty is, let's discuss some helpful tips to achieve emotional wellness.

1. Take some time off for yourself.

   We engage in many activities that make our life monotonous and put us in an unhealthy pattern where we strive all day. Organize your busy schedule and take some time to do something that brings you joy and helps distract you from your daily stressful life.

2. Surround yourself with the right people.

   Sometimes the people around us are the reason we feel so low or develop self-esteem-related issues. If the people around you make you feel uncomfortable about who you are or the way you look it is time you reconsider having them around. Every one of us deserves to be surrounded by people who cheer on us and love us just the way we are.

3. Take care of your skin.

   As mentioned above, the condition of our skin can have a major impact on our emotional wellness. Having a good skincare regime will not only give you healthier skin but will also help boost your confidence.

   Beauty is subjective and feeling beautiful is everyone's right. True beauty is loving ourselves even if how we look is far from the set beauty standards.

- **Physical wellness**

The most commonly known type of wellness is physical wellness. However, it is misunderstood to mean only being disease-free. There are many other aspects of physical wellness that we will explore going forward. Physical wellness depends on a multitude of things for example your living conditions, nutrition, habits and routine.

Many factors play into keeping your body healthy and your mind fresh, nutrition being top of the list. To quote a very famous phrase 'You are what you eat', your body depends on food to function and grow, so what you eat determines many things.

Another important factor is your routine. Having a healthy routine not only includes a stable sleep pattern and exercising but also having healthy habits. We don't realize how many of our daily habits like biting nails, staying up late or being unhygienic can be extremely unhealthy for us.

Further elaborating on unhealthy habits, substance abuse is also a very key aspect of physical wellness. Drinking too much alcohol, smoking too much, and doing drugs is very damaging to our physical health and can cause diseases.

The Importance of physical wellness

The importance of physical wellness is common knowledge. However, there is a need to reiterate it repeatedly because we often neglect our physical health due to our busy lives. Being conscious of the changes in your body is important now more than ever that we come in contact with so many harmful substances in our daily life.

Being physically well not only keeps us away from the threat of diseases but also improves our quality of life and work. If we are physically well, we will have more energy to do the things we enjoy. Being unhealthy or unwell makes us moody and can often affect our mental states as well. Physical wellness ensures that you have the strength to take on the challenges in life and enjoy them thoroughly.

How to achieve physical wellness

There's a few that you should be especially mindful of when it comes to physical wellness like,

Nutritional Needs

Taking care of your nutrition helps build immunity and ensures that you do not become deficient in certain vitamins and minerals. Women are especially prone to iron and calcium deficiencies that can cause conditions like anemia or osteoporosis. Therefore, it is important to eat healthy and timely meals.

A Proper Routine

Your sleep determines how energized you will be throughout the day. Having a healthy sleep pattern means getting at least eight hours of undisturbed sleep every night. Going to bed on time and waking up will give you a great start to your day and time for exercise. Squeeze a short workout into your daily routine so your body does not become stiff; stretching cardio can not only help you keep fit but will also increase stamina and give physical strength.

Be Responsible With Addictive Substances

Substances like alcohol, cigarettes, or drugs can be highly addictive and very dangerous to your overall health. It is important to keep your consumption in check or steer clear of them entirely.

- **Social wellness**

Social wellness refers to our social interactions and how we deal with them. It means to be comfortable with social interactions and have healthy relationships. Social wellness is a very dynamic concept. It covers every aspect of your social life. For instance, how balanced your social life is, the kind of people you surround yourself with. How you interact with people and the kind of relationships you have also determine social wellness.

When it comes to personal relationships and friendships, social wellness is a person's ability to start relationships and continue them. Being able to communicate healthily and set reasonable boundaries is also an important aspect of social wellness.

In a more general perspective, social wellness refers to how well you mingle with the people around you. This includes people in your community or co-workers. Being considerate of diversity and racial, ethnic, and religious differences and having respect for people is also a measure of social wellness.

Why Is Social Wellness Important?

Humans are social animals, which means we have the ability to communicate with others and for bonds while we co-exist.

Having meaningful relationships and a supportive network of friends makes you feel less lonely. Feelings of loneliness can often detach you from the world and cause depression, so it is important to have meaningful relationships in life.

Being comfortable around other people and having the ability to communicate is a very useful tool once we enter our professional lives. Having the ability to engage with others helps create a useful network of colleagues throughout your career. In today's world, networking is especially important for professional growth, whether you are a business owner or an employee.

How to Achieve Social Wellness

Social wellness is not only about making new friends but also ensuring the friendships or social interactions around you are healthy and don't cause you any emotional strain. Some tips to achieve social wellness are.

1. **Keep An Open Heart**

   When it comes to advising about making new friends this is perhaps the most important thing you need to keep in mind. You will find it much easier to interact with people if you keep an open mind. First meetings are often chaotic. Do not be put off by certain opinions the other person may have and be accepting.

2. **Cut Off The Toxic People In Your Life**

   Time cannot determine the quality of a relationship by the time you have put into them. Some old friendships can be very toxic for us and cause a lot of emotional trauma. But we often don't realize this and let ourselves suffer. Surrounding yourself with good people is also a form of self-care.

3. Learn To Create Boundaries

Some relationships in our life consume too much of our energy and time.

It is important to create reasonable boundaries so that your interactions do not overwhelm you. A good way to do this is by communicating and learning to stand up for yourself.

4. Try To Maintain A Balance

It is important to maintain a balance in social interactions. Just like less social interaction is bad, too much social interaction can also harm you. It drains out your energy and gives you no personal time. It is important to maintain a healthy balance in your social life.

- **Intellectual wellness**

Amongst the numerous types of wellness, a very important but often overlooked type is intellectual wellness. Contrary to popular belief, intellect does not have much to do with doing well academically. In its true meaning, intellectual wellness means developing critical thinking skills and healthy learning patterns.

Some other ways to describe intellectual wellness is understanding new concepts, being able to think through difficult problems and being able to manage academics can also be intellectual wellness. A very important aspect of intellectual wellness is challenging your mind by exposing it to new material and exercises.

For the layman, we can also say the desire to have exposure and learn more is also an aspect of intellectual wellness. Being curious and understanding what one learns academically so that they can apply it to real life is what intellectual wellness truly is.

Why is it important?

Most people think the development of our mind stops after a certain age, which may be true in terms of physical growth, however another type of brain development is the development of neural networks. When a person comes across a challenging task that requires mental work and critical thinking they form strong neural networks which in turn slows down a person's cognitive decline.

Intellectual wellness is very important because it helps us constantly improve and enhance our learning abilities. It helps us develop a deeper understanding of whatever it is that we may be curious to know. Intellectual wellness stems from curiosity which can help us not only engage in important conversations but also become more respectful of other schools of thought.

Most importantly, intellectual wellness helps us discover our true potential, and not everyone has the same learning interests and strength however our educational systems put us all in one box. Having the desire and curiosity to discover and learn new things can help us figure out our true passion. It will help us choose meaningful professions and do work that not only pays the bills but also feeds the soul.

Ways to achieve intellectual wellness.

The path to intellectual wellness is a slow and difficult tone because it requires a lot of work, but we can encourage it by a small act like,

1. **Reading**

   Reading is the best way to absorb new information, develop a habit of something on a topic that interests you. Reading books is great; however you can also find newsletters or short essays if a book seems too much.

2. **Indulge in something challenging.**

   Challenging your mind from time to time gets it working. Hobbies like chess or crossword puzzles, or other challenging games are a great way.

3. **Participate in conversations.**

   Join a group or start conversations about meaningful topics that can give you more exposure; participating in intellectual conversations helps you learn new things and also may introduce you to newer perspectives.

4. **Learn a new language.**

   Learning a language is often difficult in adulthood; it greatly stimulates the mind and language is also a helpful skill.

   Intellectual wellness is truly important but often overlooked by us, and we must push our minds to their limit and improve constantly.

- **Environmental wellness**

Environmental wellness has two aspects to it, the actual physical environment and your environment. The physical environment is the earth, climate and how its condition directly affects us, and your personal environment is the social environment in which you exist. As we all know everything that exists in an ecosystem is co-dependent which means our physical environment greatly affects our wellbeing and vice versa.

Unsustainable human practices have destroyed the natural ecosystem of the earth, and pollution has accelerated and worsened climate change. These changes affect us directly; for example, the deteriorating air quality is causing an array of respiratory illnesses and skin-related allergies.

So what is environmental wellness?

Environmental wellness in its true meaning is to live in harmony with your environment. It means living more sustainably and making small changes to your lifestyle so that you contribute less to polluting it. Reducing your carbon footprint is another way to put it.

Living in harmony with your environment can also mean appreciating it and using it to achieve personal wellness, like taking walks or interacting more with nature. A morning run in the park or getting some fresh air and instantly lightening up a person's mood, also helps clear your mind.

Environmental wellness is very important; it not only makes you more aware of your impact on the environment but also gives you a sense of responsibility which encourages a healthier and more suitable lifestyle. It helps you realize that you are part of something bigger and that you can actively contribute to making the world a better place.

How to achieve environmental wellness

Now that we know how important environmental wellness is, let's discuss how we can effectively achieve it; the key is to start small and be persistent. Do not rush yourself into it; changing habits is often hard and rushing into something makes you uncomfortable and may not last long.

1. **Educate Yourself**

   The first step to achieve environmental wellness is to become aware of how your lifestyle may be damaging to the environment. Educating yourself will help you monitor yourself and make relevant changes.

2. **Cut down on the excess.**

   I believe the best way to start is to cut down on what you feel is excess in terms of consumption. Stopping yourself is easier than building a new habit. One example is reducing your use of plastic, especially single-use plastics.

3. **Walk where you can.**

   Traveling short distances on a vehicle greatly harms the environment. A better alternative would be to start cycling or walking. Both of these options are healthier and much more sustainable. Switching to public transport (if feasible) is also a great option.

4. Reuse and Recycle.

Make a habit out of reusing things where possible, like containers to store food or to keep a mug for your coffee. Recycling things is known to be one of the most effective ways to deal with waste; there are many useful resources online that guide beginners on how to start and what to do.

Achieving environmental wellness or even starting to live more consciously is a beautiful journey that gives inner satisfaction. We must protect the earth and let it heal.

• Spiritual wellness

A much-overlooked type of wellness is spiritual wellness. We are often quick to realize if something is wrong with our body or mind. However we don't usually pay attention to our spirit.

The best way to describe it would be being in peace. It is evident in many ways like finding a purpose in life or being one with yourself. However, for beginners, we could say spiritual wellness can mean that you are content. The opposite of spiritual wellness is feeling empty or lost.

It is a known fact that spiritual wellness is connected to a god or religion. Yes, for some people spirituality does mean believing in religion or having faith. However, this is just one aspect of spiritual wellness. Some people believe defeating our inner demons or finding a balance between our id and superego is spirituality. All of this is true; we are constantly in battle with ourselves and the outside world and finding spiritual wellness is acceptance and contentment.

Why Is Spiritual Wellness Important?

Spiritual wellness is important because, without our spirit, we are nothing but empty beings striving for material gains and artificial happiness. Being in touch with our inner selves gives us purpose and true happiness. It helps us appreciate how beautiful life is and makes us look past the material life.

Spiritual wellness also plays a very strong role in giving some people a sense of morality and ethics. People find morality and principles through belief systems. It is possible that spiritual wellness makes people more considerate and keeps them moralized.

Being in touch with your inner self also helps you stay in touch with nature and who you are as a person. Often we lose touch with the world and just exist for the sake of it. A healthy spirit keeps us alive and keeps us going.

How to Achieve Spiritual Wellness

Contrary to popular belief, you do not necessarily need to have a religious revelation to get in touch with your spirit. Some easier ways to obtain spiritual wellness are.

1. Help Others

Sometimes all we need is a sense of togetherness to get in touch with ourselves. Although all of us have our struggles when we feel extremely detached, acts of kindness like volunteering and helping someone in need can bring us back.

2. Meditate

Meditation is the best and most foolproof method to get in touch with our inner selves and recharge our spirits. It feels difficult sometimes and requires a lot of focus and practice but trying never hurts.

3. Do something You Love.

Things that keep the spirit alive are art and literature. Take some out for yourself and indulge in some soul searching with art whether you do it yourself or just admire someone else's work. Writing or reading poetry can also recharge your soul.

4. Go On A Trip

Sometimes all we need is to get away from our stagnant environment and explore to recharge our soul. Traveling is not only super fun but also gives you great memories and time for yourself.

Although we live busy lives and seldom have time for ourselves, it is important to pause and look into your spirit. We must keep our spirit alive to feel alive.

- **Occupational wellness**

If we put occupational wellness in one sentence, it would be 'Our job does not necessarily have to be a struggle; the hustle can also be healthy.' There are a few aspects to occupational wellness; the most important factor is the impact of occupation on you. At the end of the day how does your job make you feel? If you feel a sense of achievement and satisfaction, you're on the right path. We spend a lot of our time and energy at work which is why it is important that our occupation makes us happy and challenges our abilities.

Another important factor that concerns occupation wellness is the environment of your workplace and your relationship with colleagues. If the environment of your workplace is toxic, it will negatively affect your mental health. Being surrounded by co-workers who encourage you and provide healthy completion is an important determinant of occupational wellness.

The Importance of Occupational Wellness

Being happy with your job and finding fulfillment in what you do is very important. Dissatisfaction with our career can cause unhappiness which majorly affects productivity. Occupational wellness ensures that you are satisfied with what you do and inspired to achieve bigger success.

Imagine being stuck in a job that has no prospects of personal growth. A career path that does not enable you to enhance your abilities and limits your growth is like being put in a box. It can be very suffocating and seriously harms one's creativity. The same goes with having a toxic work environment; it brings down your spirits and suffocates you.

One important aspect of occupational wellness is work-life balance; it is crucial for your mental and physical health to have a healthy balance. Taking time for yourself and indulging in hobbies will create a healthy living pattern and keep you fresh.

How to Achieve Occupational Wellness

There are a few ways to achieve occupational wellness.

1. **Look Forward To Growth**

   When you become comfortable with your pace, it means you are no longer growing. Stagnant work will become boring after some time. Challenge yourself from time to time and learn new skills to always be at a healthy pace.

2. **Maintain A Good Relationship With Co-Workers**

   This point is especially important because co-workers play a huge role in determining how your time at the office will be. Having a good relationship means you have mutual respect and people to go to for assistance.

3. **Do Meaningful Work**

   The definition of meaningful work is different for everyone. Think about what inspires and interests you, and then pursue it. A majority of us are stuck in jobs that make us miserable. However, we continue because they pay the bills. Occupational wellness means finding fulfillment in our work.

4. **Maintain A Healthy Balance**

   Overworking is unhealthy. Find time for leisure and personal activities so that you stay energized and do not become stressed out.

   Work is an important chunk of our lives. It is what we invest most of our time doing, so we must make occupational wellness a priority.

• **Financial wellness**

Wellness is a term that in recent times expanded in both meaning and scope. The trajectory of wellness that began with talking about physical wellbeing is present in mental and emotional wellness by the World Health Organization in the year 1946. In recent times, wellness gurus have realized that there are many financial dimensions of wellness that need to be taken into account for a holistic definition of wellness.

Let us understand the concept of financial wellbeing and how we can ensure good health for our finances.

What is financial wellness, and why is it important?

Financial wellness is a vital concept though is highly underrated. The way we live has a deep impact on our health and is influenced the robustness of our economies. Money influences every sphere of our life. Job, lifestyle, education, access to healthcare, nutrition, and housing, nothing remains untouched. Not having enough finances diminishes the overall quality of life-giving rise to all sorts of physical and mental issues.

How can you attain financial wellness?

Having resilient fiscal health is critical for your financial wellbeing. All you have to do is follow a few steps to build the health of your finances.

* ***Budgeting:*** Budgeting is the very foundation of financial wellness. Developing a budget is an important lesson in spending within your means. A budget inculcates a habit of

responsible expenditure by making short and long-term financial goals.

* ***Responsible Spending:*** Making a budget is only the first step. What is more important is to adhere to it. A periodic review of your spending as against the available/allocated budget would allow you to make a course correction in the event of a splurge or unforeseen expense.

* ***Savings:*** Life hardly pans out the way we want it. There would always be twists and turns in the form of emergencies. It could be excruciatingly difficult to manage when an emergency knocks at your door if you don't have enough resources saved up to take care of rainy days.

  No saving is a small saving, and every penny counts. When you prepare your budget, make sure to save some amount from the overall income. You may not need the money right away, but letting your savings build up over time would help you when you need the resources.

* ***Financial consultant:*** Financial wellness is a subject matter that needs an expert to advise. It is best that you seek advice from a certificated financial advisor. A financial advisor is at a best-placed position to help you plan your financial wellness as per your requirements.

  You have to be smart, not rich, to have strong financial wellness. Plan effectively and lead a stress-free life.

  Now, you have seen the eight dimensions of wellness and must accept the reality that your health is as delicate as a flower. For it to blossom, you must nurture it properly so that it can contribute to your general well-being.

"The only way to achieve this balance is to feel good about ourselves by promoting good habits and routines".

Wellness Self-Assessment

A good starting point to live a balanced and meaningful life is to evaluate your current state in different areas of your wellness. See in which area you are thriving and where you need to pay more attention.

The Wellness Self-Assessment of 8 Areas is a tool created and reproduced based on SAMHSA (Substance Abuse and Mental Health Services Administration) Wellness Initiative

Answer all the questions for each of the eight wellness dimensions. Total your points for each section and use the guide to interpret the scores.

PHYSICAL	Rarely, if Ever	Some-times	Most of the time	Always
I maintain a desirable weight	1	2	3	4
I engage in vigorous exercises for over 30 minutes a day (i.e., brisk walking, cycling) up to 5 times a week and strengthening exercises two or more days a week.	1	2	3	4
I get 7-8 hours of sleep each night, and awake feeling refreshed.	1	2	3	4
I listen to my body; when there is something wrong, I seek professional advice.	1	2	3	4
I abstain from drug abuse, both over-the-counter (OTC) and illicit.	1	2	3	4
I responsibly use alcohol. (i.e., designating sober drivers and avoiding binge drinking).	1	2	3	4
I know my important health numbers: cholesterol, blood pressure, blood glucose, body weight, etc.	1	2	3	4
I protect my skin from sun damage by using sunscreen, wearing hats, and avoiding tanning booths and sun lamps.	1	2	3	4
I eat at least five servings of fresh fruits and vegetables daily and drink water regularly.	1	2	3	4
I protect myself from STDs or unwanted pregnancy by either abstaining from sexual behavior or using proper protection such as condoms.	1	2	3	4
TOTAL				

EMOTIONAL	Rarely, if Ever	Some-times	Most of the time	Always
I can ask for assistance when I need it, from either friends and family or professionals.	1	2	3	4
I can recognize the stressors in my life and have ways to reduce those stressors.	1	2	3	4
I accept responsibility for my actions.	1	2	3	4
I can set priorities.	1	2	3	4
I try to avoid chronic worry, and I am not usually suspicious of others.	1	2	3	4
I feel good about myself and believe others like me for who I am.	1	2	3	4
I am flexible and adapt or adjust to life's challenges positively.	1	2	3	4
I can express all ranges of feelings (i.e. hurt, sadness, fear, anger, and joy) and manage related behaviors in a healthy way.	1	2	3	4
I maintain balance of work, family, friends, and other obligations	1	2	3	4
I do not let my emotions get the better of me and I think before I act.	1	2	3	4
TOTAL				

OCCUPATIONAL	Rarely, if Ever	Some-times	Most of the time	Always
I balance work with play and other aspects of my life.	1	2	3	4
I take advantage of opportunities to learn new skills, which will enhance my future employment possibilities.	1	2	3	4
I know what skills are necessary for the occupations I am interested in.	1	2	3	4
I Strive to develop good work habits. (Examples: punctuality, dependability, and initiative).	1	2	3	4
Enjoyment is a consideration I use when choosing a possible career.	1	2	3	4
I work effectively with others.	1	2	3	4
I am developing the necessary skills to achieve my career goals.	1	2	3	4
I have confidence in my job search skills (resume writing, interviewing, etc.).	1	2	3	4
I have explored different career options.	1	2	3	4
I know where to find employment if needed. (job service, online resources).	1	2	3	4
TOTAL				

SOCIAL	Rarely, if Ever	Some-times	Most of the time	Always
I am involved in at least one university or community group.	1	2	3	4
I plan time with family and friends.	1	2	3	4
I enjoy the time I spend with others.	1	2	3	4
I respect the diversity of others (i.e., race, ethnicity, religion, gender, ability, orsexual orientation).	1	2	3	4
I give priority to my own needs by saying 'no' to others' requests of me when applicable.	1	2	3	4
I participate in a wide variety of social activities and enjoy being with people who are different than me.	1	2	3	4
I try to be a "better person" and work on behaviors that have caused problems in my interactions with others.	1	2	3	4
I have someone I can talk to about my private feelings.	1	2	3	4
I consider how what I say might be perceived by others before I speak.	1	2	3	4
I give and take equally in cooperative relationships.	1	2	3	4
TOTAL				

ENVIRONMENTAL	Rarely, if Ever	Some-times	Most of the time	Always
I am concerned about environmental pollution and actively try to preserve and protect natural resources.	1	2	3	4
If I see a safety hazard, I take the steps to fix the problem	1	2	3	4
I reduce, reuse, and recycle products.	1	2	3	4
I live with the awareness of wholeness and the interconnectedness of all living systems.	1	2	3	4
I use both sides of the paper when taking class notes or doing assignments.	1	2	3	4
I have adopted water saving habits (i.e. I try not to leave the faucet running too long when I wash dishes, brush my teeth, shave, or bathe).	1	2	3	4
I participate in campus events that help my community. (Food drives, fundraisers, planting trees, disaster relief, Habitat for Humanity).	1	2	3	4
I spend time outdoors enjoying nature.	1	2	3	4
I use ecologically friendly products (i.e. eco-friendly cleaning supplies, organic products, energy efficient appliances), whenever possible.	1	2	3	4
I walk, bike, use public transportation or carpool.	1	2	3	4
TOTAL				

SPIRITUAL	Rarely, if Ever	Some-times	Most of the time	Always
I have a deep appreciation for the depth of life, death and understanding universal human connection or consciousness.	1	2	3	4
I recognize that there are many spiritual paths and that every spiritual tradition recognizes and teaches basic precepts or laws of wise and conscious human conduct while seeking qualities of altruism, optimism, hope and forgiveness.	1	2	3	4
I integrate my "spiritual practice" within everyday life of work, family and relationships.	1	2	3	4
I make time for relaxation in my day.	1	2	3	4
I take time alone to think about what's important in life - who I am, what I value, where I fit in, and where I'm going.	1	2	3	4
I have faith in a greater power, be it a God-like force, or something else.	1	2	3	4
I work for peace in my interpersonal relationships, in my community, and in the world at large.	1	2	3	4
My values guide my decisions and actions.	1	2	3	4
I have a sense of purpose in my life.	1	2	3	4
I am accepting of the views of others.	1	2	3	4
TOTAL				

FINANCIAL	Rarely, if Ever	Some-times	Most of the time	Always
I always have the money for what I need.	1	2	3	4
I review my bank statements when I receive them.	1	2	3	4
I pay all of my bills on time.	1	2	3	4
I balance or reconcile my bank accounts regularly.	1	2	3	4
I keep my Social Security Card or Number in a secure place.	1	2	3	4
I save part of my income every time I receive any money (from work, family, gifts, or refunds of any kind).	1	2	3	4
I pay my credit card bill off completely every month.	1	2	3	4
I check my credit report to look for any errors (TransUnion, Experian, or Equifax).	1	2	3	4
I follow a spending plan every month.	1	2	3	4
Every time I get a new Debit card I change the PIN (Personal Identification Number).	1	2	3	4
TOTAL				

INTELLECTUAL	Rarely, if Ever	Some-times	Most of the time	Always
I seek personal growth by learning new skills.	1	2	3	4
I listen to ideas different from my own and constantly re-examine my judgments on social, cultural, age, gender, religion, sexual orientation, race, disability, national origin, ethical, and political issues.	1	2	3	4
I look for ways to use my creativity and critical thinking skills.	1	2	3	4
I am open to new ideas.	1	2	3	4
I keep informed about social, political and/or current issues.	1	2	3	4
I watch educational programs on television every week, (News, political discussions, documentaries, public TV, or the Discovery channel).	1	2	3	4
I learn about different topics that interest me from books, magazines, newspapers, and the Internet.	1	2	3	4
Before making decisions, I gather facts.	1	2	3	4
I know about available campus resources in my area of study.	1	2	3	4
I know how to access academic resources when necessary.	1	2	3	4
TOTAL				

Disclaimer: The scores on the Wellness Self-Assessment do not reflect any particular diagnosis or course of treatment. It is intended for individual level self-reflection and goal setting.

Scores of 20-28: Wonderful! You are taking positive steps in this dimension of wellness. You achieved a high overall score in this area. Check for low scores on individual items or other wellness areas to see for any enhancement.

Scores of 15-19: Your wellness score in this area is good, but there is room for improvement. Take a look at the items on which you scored lower. Even a change in behavior can help you achieve better health and well-being.

Scores of 14 and below: Your answers indicate some potential well-being risks in that domain of wellness. Review those areas where you scored lower and focus on developing and setting achievable goals.

PART THREE

SKIN-FRIENDLY HABITS:
6 KEYS FOR A HEALTHY SKIN

"Healthy skin is a reflection of
overall wellness."
Dr. Murad

Y ou desire to have skin that glows, right? Of course, everyone wants the perfect skin that radiates and glows beautifully. But the question is do you have the patience to feed your skin well? Now, here is the big problem. I discovered that everyone wants the perfect skin but find it difficult to do what it entails to get their ideal skin. Trust me, and I was comfortable in that position before now.

Looking for beauty and maintaining your skin is not made a reality by mere wishes and desires. No, it is a lifestyle. To maintain this lifestyle, you must keep it simple and sustainable. While I was much younger, I felt there was no need to pay attention to my skin and look into the mirror for 10-15 minutes every day. So, I settled for a beauty routine I could manage effortlessly. The matter of fact was that I enjoyed myself while going about my skincare routine.

I came back to the basics - Only the essential things my skin needed, which were affordable, simple and sustainable that I can effortlessly make room in my everyday life. It was the lifestyle I chose for myself, and it worked like magic!

Dr. Robert Kim, a skincare specialist, emphasizes the importance of having a beautiful lifestyle to patients at his skincare clinic in Chungdam located at Gangnam, Seoul Korea which is the hub of K-Beauty. So, asides from suggesting aesthetic procedures to his beauty-conscious patients, he advocates for living a healthy lifestyle such as drinking enough water, exercising, wellness routine and consuming lots of minerals and vitamins.

I am willing to share all the information Dr. Robert Kim suggests for healthy skin. These important keys are in seven different forms. Are you curious? Read on to find out!

1. Hydration

Hydration is incredibly important for your entire body and, at the end of the day, even for your soul. As with many other things- consistency is key. Sufficient hydration is one of the key ingredients when it comes to beautiful, glowing, and plump skin. It is essentially an internal moisturizer. Skin is your largest organ and just like any other organ it needs sufficient water. Water improves circulation and prevents flaky and dry skin. It can even prevent wrinkles!

- *Tips on how to drink more water.*

a. Use a Tracker.

Some people are very goal-oriented and motivated by badges, awards, or simply seeing their progress jolted down on a piece of paper. You can use an old-school method of tally marks or use one of the many habit tracking apps.

b. Flavor Your Water

We all know sugary drinks aren't good for us, but if you are having trouble transitioning to just water maybe try adding some flavor. Water with fruit is surprisingly delicious and slightly sweet, just enough to satisfy your craving. You can add lemons, limes, mint, or even berries.

c. Set a Reminder.

You can use an alarm, an app, or even a friend. Setting a reminder is a great step if you want to drink more water but forget doing it. Regular reminders will help you establish a healthy routine which after a while will make it feel almost like a reflex.

d. Eat Your Water

As funny as this one might sound, it's effective and simple to do. Soups, stews, most vegetables and fruits are all foods or meals that contain a lot of water. Not only are they good in that respect, but they also fill you up and are usually jam-packed with vitamins and minerals that make your skin truly glow.

e. Don't Force It

If you are overly ambitious and prefer to chug down jugs of water, you won't achieve the desired effect, and you might even feel sick. If you're struggling with your water intake it might be a better idea to start by simply pouring yourself a glass of water and sipping on it. You can then refill it every one to two hours and it will never seem like a chore again.

f. Use "Bad" Habits to Your Advantage

If you can't live without a consistent dose of caffeine or if you drink alcohol on a fairly regular basis, you can somewhat offset some of the negative effects by simply drinking a glass of refreshing water with another beverage of choice. Not only will your skin look better, but also bad hangovers will be a thing of the past.

2. Healthy eating

The importance of eating healthy meals cannot be overemphasized well, you have heard you are what you eat, so your choice of food affects the way your skin looks.

The most obvious points to note for food–skin connection are allergies and even milder intolerances. They can cause rashes, pimples, and dull and itchy skin.

Fruits and vegetables are incredibly important because they provide us with plenty of vitamins and minerals. However, some other nutrients are available to keep your skin youthful and fresh looking, so make sure you eat healthy (omega-3) fats and antioxidant and water-filled food.

"Fruits and vegetables are incredibly important
because they provide us with plenty of vitamins and
minerals"

- *Dietary rules to keep your skin glowing and healthy.*

a. ***Choose Whole Grains:*** I know it doesn't sound too appealing at first, but "whole" foods can be an acquired taste. It might be hard to swap out at first, but after a while, you will prefer a nice, filling, and slightly tangy rye bread to a simple and bland white bread. Simple isn't always bad but each grain has its unique taste that is lost during the processing.

Whole grains also contain more antioxidants, and if your wholegrain bread has seeds mixed in, even quite a few healthy fats. Not only will whole grains make your skin look better, but your body (especially your digestion and cardiovascular system) will be eternally thankful for the daily dose of healthy fiber.

b. ***Choose Whole Vegetables and Fruits:*** What I mean by that is that it's a much healthier option to simply eat the entire fruit instead of drinking gallons of sugary juices. Sugar can be one of the worst things you could eat in general, but it also applies to your skin.

Sugar is a pure carbohydrate that can weaken your immune system and cause inflammation in your body and consequently affect your skin. It can cause acne. It can break down collagen that makes your skin look and feel youthful. If your only option is drinking a freshly squeezed juice instead of eating a salad, it's still a good idea to get those vitamins in; just try not to make it a habit. Salads, fruits, and even smoothies are healthier, more sustainable, and more satisfying anyway.

c. ***Don't Buy into "Diet Culture":*** Diet in and of itself is not a bad thing. The real issue is "diet culture" that focuses on fad diets that promise miracles but simply aren't sustainable in the long run. Extremes aren't good for the vast majority of people. No healthy fats can make your skin look dull and unhealthy. Carbs are important because they provide you with energy and enough of the incredibly important fiber. Protein is the building block of your skin and also a key component of a healthy diet. It also keeps your hormones in check and prevents hormonal acne. If your diet is balanced and nourishing, your skin will be balanced and nourished.

And as with most things in life, moderation is key.

3. Cleansing skin

Cleansing your skin is one of the most important keys to living a friendly lifestyle for your skin. In your daily interaction and activities, you expose your skin to many unpleasant chemicals and substances. These chemicals, in turn, wreak havoc on your skin.

- ***Four reasons for cleansing your skin.***

a. ***It Removes Dirt and Prevents Skin Issues:*** Makeup, excessive oil, pollution, dead skin cells, and other things that accumulate on your face throughout the day can cause a surprising amount of issues if you don't take care of your skin and cleanse it properly at the end of the day. Clogged pores can be a breeding ground for bacteria that causes pimples, blackheads, whiteheads and other issues. Cleansing your skin is especially important if you use makeup. Even if you don't, stuff still accumulates on your skin throughout the day and that is why I truly do believe that most, if not all people should thoroughly cleanse their face at least once, but preferably twice a day.

b. ***It Makes Your Skin Look Better Overall:*** Not only does cleansing your skin prevent acne and other issues, but it's also simply healthier looking overall. Washing your face hydrates, rejuvenates, and freshens up your face. It makes it look less dull and more radiant. It gets your circulation going and encourages cell renewal. If leaving makeup on is a habit it can even lead to permanently enlarged pores which are an even bigger magnet for all kinds of debris. Making sure your face is completely clean before you go to bed will make your skin look glowing, youthful, and plump and allow it to put all the energy into rejuvenating and regenerating itself.

c. ***It Helps Your Skin Absorb Everything Else You Put On It:*** It's much easier for your moisturizer, serums, masks, and other skincare products to penetrate and nurture your skin if you clean it beforehand. Cleansers remove not only external pollutants, but also excessive sebum (natural skin oil) stuck inside your pores and allows your skin to soak up all the goodness from the other products you use afterward. Sebum in and of itself is by no means a "bad guy" but excessive amounts can cause a plethora of issues.

d. ***It is a Form of Relaxation:*** I like to think of the entire skincare routine as a relaxing evening (and morning) ritual that allows me to process the day as I go through the motions. It's a soothing habit that doesn't only affect my skin but my mind as well. Look at it as a gentle face massage that will nurture both your skin and your soul and a time to let go. Of course it's always the best option to use skincare that is natural, organic, sustainable, and that suits your skin, but there are a lot of affordable cleansers available that check all the marks.

4. Moisturizing skin

It is the fourth key to living a healthy lifestyle for your skin. There are too many benefits of moisturizing your skin. If you desire healthy, fresh and youthful skin, the key to achieving this is to moisturize your skin. Moisture deficiency reduces collagen production and collagen is the main reason the skin looks younger.

When you moisturize your skin, it prevents wrinkles and fine lines from appearing on your skin. Moisturized and hydrated skin looks and feels plump, firm, and gives you a wonderfully fresh glow. Moisturizers also reinforce your skin's natural strength and protect it from environmental factors, especially if it contains additional protective and nourishing ingredients (such as SPF, vitamins, and antioxidants.) Even if your skin is on the oily side, you should use a quality moisturizing product, and it will keep your skin balanced regardless of if it's dry or oily.

Moisturizers also help your skin feel better. Dry and flaky skin can be very irritating and uncomfortable. Moisturizing products are one of the most important parts of skincare and it especially pays off to be consistent and try to use it daily.

5. Protecting your skin

When you love something or someone, what do you do? You protect them! It also applies to your skin. When you love your skin, you do everything properly for it to stay healthy. To protect your skin from unfriendly elements, make use of sunscreen. There are two different types of sunscreens, chemical and physical (mineral).

Chemical sunscreen is a good choice if you want something durable and waterproof, and it also absorbs faster. Physical sunscreen is ideal for sensitive skin because it sits on your skin and does not cause irritation on the skin. But, if you are in a situation where you don't have access to sunscreen, try your best to stay in the shade, cover your skin, and wear a hat that keeps sun rays away from your face. However, vitamin D is very important for the skin. So, try as much as you can to enjoy the beauty of the sun's rays but make sure it is in moderation. You do not have to spend hours upon hours lying in the scorching sun; 15-20 minutes (avoid it between 10 AM and 4 PM) daily should do.

Avoid harsh products and seek out gentle products that won't completely strip your skin of its natural oils. Cleanse your skin as often as you should but do not overdo it. Using a gentle cleanser once or twice a day (evening or morning) is enough. Ensure also to live a healthy life such as exercising, proper dieting, and hydration and avoid any form of stress.

Most importantly, get to know the type of skin that you have. Different skin types need different skincare products. Everyone should use a moisturizer, but some might need a lighter gel water-based one and others a thicker one that will nourish and protect dry skin. Those with combination skin might need more than one product if they have an oily t-zone and very dry cheeks. Also, pay attention to how your skin reacts to products and skincare routine.

6. Mindful skincare

Mindful skincare is a wonderful way to not only help your skin feel better but also a useful and convenient technique to reduce stress. Creating small and comforting rituals in your day-to-day life can be a great, simple, and quick way to take care of not only your skin but your mind as well. You can think of it as meditation. It is a few minutes daily to focus on a specific thing and simply go through the motions while paying attention to all the sensations that arise.

Looking in the mirror and appreciating everything you see can be such a beautiful and healing process. When you do this, you are bound to start thinking of your skincare to cherish yourself instead of taking it as just another chore that is an inevitable part of your life. When you let go of the outside world and focus on the things that concern you, you start appreciating your true beauty.

Your beauty routine can be the time to appreciate everything you are - inside and out. Making yourself a priority for at least a few minutes a day will make it easier to share yourself the rest of the day. You are allowed to take care of your appearance, your health, and ultimately your entire being. If you would like to experience a soothing mindfulness meditation, please feel free to listen to our RESPEKT beauty routine meditation sessions.

Beauty With The Helpful Ingredients

The purpose of using cosmetics is to supply the ingredients our skin needs. Our skin is different from one another, and the specific ingredients our skin needs depending on age, climate, skin problem and basic skin types and stress levels. The skincare industry is all about the ingredients and how the brands approach our skin with what packaging and marketing method.

We live in a world with a whole collection of beauty products, and we truly are lucky enough to have something that our skin needs.

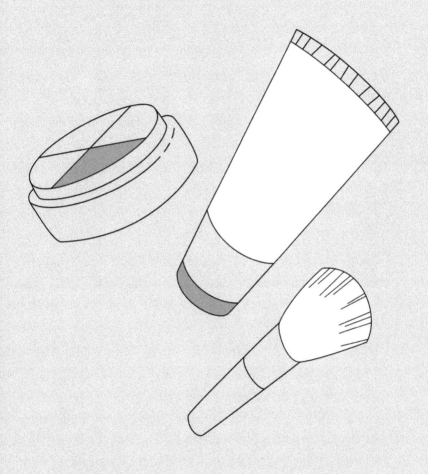

"Your beauty routine can be the time to appreciate
everything you are - inside and out."

The hard part is to know what the right ingredient and product for me is out of millions of products. The biggest problem is when feeding the needed ingredients to our skin, and harmful ingredients can accompany whether it was to keep the product last longer or to make the formula blend better with other ingredients.

From my experience with beauty products, I have come to accept that the best types of beauty products to use are skin-friendly products. Plant-based products are the most common beauty products to use because they nourish the skin and give it a healthy look.

Some beauty products contain carcinogenic ingredients, causing allergy, and these types of products are not wellness-rooted beauty products. So, from my perception, the safest products are products that do not contain harsh chemicals that may harm the skin.

Natural, organic, and vegan cosmetics are becoming more and more popular, and with good reason– harsh chemicals can cause skin sensitivity, dermatitis, hormonal imbalances, and some are even carcinogenic. Clean, healthy, nourishing, vegan, and natural products are not only better for your health, but they are less harmful to animals and of course, the environment.

Skin Loving Ingredients

Are there beauty products that contain friendly chemicals? The answer is an emphatic YES. Some of the helpful chemicals that is good for healthy skin. They are:

1. Salicylic acid

Salicylic acid is a fairly gentle but incredibly effective acid. It can significantly reduce acne, blackheads, and even dandruff. If you are overproducing sebum, this one is a great choice.

2. Hyaluronic acid

Hyaluronic acid is produced by your body. Products containing it can heal atopic dermatitis and hydrate your dry skin, making it more youthful and plump.

3. Peptides

Peptides make your skin more taut and smooth. It's one of the ingredients that can help you lessen the appearance of wrinkles and fine lines.

4. Lauric Acid

Lauric acid is naturally found in coconut oil and has incredible   antibacterial and moisturizing properties. It is great for acne-prone or inflamed skin.

5. Alpha Hydroxy Acids (AHA)

Alpha Hydroxy Acids are great for anyone struggling with hyper-pigmentation, fine lines, and enlarged pores. One of the best age care ingredients.

6. Sunscreen

There are two types of sunscreens, those with a chemical filter and those with a physical mineral filter. I believe that the benefits of using sunscreen outweigh any potential negative side effects (such as clogged pores). Even if you do find that one type doesn't suit you, there are different formulations, and I am certain anyone can find the right one for them.

7. Retinol

Retinol is another acid that can be incredibly beneficial when used as a part of your skincare routine. It encourages cell renewal, collagen production and makes your skin look younger and healthier.

Skin Harsh Ingredients

1. Sodium lauryl sulfate (SLS)

SLS is a ubiquitous ingredient. It is an effective but harsh detergent that can dry out your skin or even cause an allergic reaction. It also dries out your hair and strips it of its natural protective oils. It is present in shampoo, soap and other cleaning products.

2. Parabens

Parabens are preservatives that can cause allergic revelations and have links to hormonal imbalances. They are not dangerous in small quantities, but I would still choose a healthier alternative when possible. They are present in almost everything from soaps, moisturizers and shampoo.

3. Phthalates

Phthalates are endocrine disruptors that can affect your metabolism, hormones, and eventually even your fertility. It has connections to ADHD, obesity, neurological issues, and more. It is also a possible carcinogen. It is present in nail polish, perfume and moisturizer.

4. Fragrance

Artificial fragrances can cause severe irritation and a lot of them contain the above-mentioned phthalates. It can cause hormonal issues, fertility issues and allergies. Another overlooked fact is that fragrances are not only an essential component of perfumes; the vast majority of cosmetic products contain fragrance.

This ingredient can be especially problematic because cosmetic companies are not required to disclose which particular fragrance they have used. RESPEKT products and we as a company are always transparent. We pride ourselves on the fact that we only use natural and high-quality fragrances. It is present in everything scented.

5. Formaldehyde

Formaldehyde is a preservative that prevents bacterial growth, and it has its place in certain fields, but you should avoid it when it comes to skincare and makeup. It has links to allergic reactions, weakened immune systems, and even cancers. It is in eyelash glue, lotion and hair gel.

6. Lead

Lead has a long history of use in cosmetics. It's also one of the worst offenders on this list. Lead can eventually cause serious damage to most organs, including your brain. Luckily it's getting used less and less, but if you find it on the ingredient list of a cosmetic product, I suggest you steer clear of it. It is found mainly in lipsticks.

7. Dimethicone

This silicone is not necessarily as dangerous as the other ingredients on this list, but it can still cause clogged pores and acne. Silicones also have a very distinct texture that can be bothersome to some. It is in conditioners and some moisturizers.

Skin-Friendly Beauty Trends

Imagine yourself constantly going like a hamster on a wheel. Tiring, isn't it? And then you pause! Stop breathing and relax. Sleep, rest, a lazy holiday, or just a cup of coffee re-energizes you to face the world once again! Extend the same logic to your skin. Your skin is its doctor, yes but even hard-working doctors need to rest.

Rejuvenation Of Our Skin- What Is The Need?

We already know the harmful effects of pollution on our skin. But how many of us know that stress is equally damaging? What makes it worse is, together, pollution and stress damage the skin beyond our comprehension. Our skin functions properly when it is hydrated. Otherwise, it becomes dry, itchy; we also develop fine lines, sunspots, dark circles, etc., which makes our skin look dull. These are signs that your skin needs to rejuvenate itself. How our skin looks tells us a lot about our health.

Tired skin is both the cause and a consequence of your mental health. Having healthy, hydrated skin not only looks good, but it's a sign of your emotional and mental wellbeing.

"*Tired skin is both the cause and a consequence of your mental health*"

The skincare and wellness space is brimming with innovations to provide various options for skin rejuvenation.

Blue Beauty Is The Next Generation Green.

Green beauty must be a familiar term if you keep up with the evolving beauty trends. There is news for you! Gone are days of the beauty trends being monochrome. There is another color added to it now. From green to blue, the beauty and skincare industry has just a step further in being environmentally conscious.

- **Blue beauty: What is it?**

While the philosophy behind green beauty is about an end-to-end transparency of the ingredients from sourcing to distribution, blue beauty goes beyond just transparency. The term blue beauty was coined by Jeannie Jarnot spearheaded Project Blue Beauty to refer to using methods and products that contribute to conserving the delicate balance of marine life.

Packaging and the normalization of harmful chemicals in beauty products is the main offender when it comes to the ocean. Packaging, most of which is excessive and wasteful and ends up at the bottom of the ocean. Going plastic-free or adopting zero-waste packaging is how blue beauty contributes to the ocean and its aquatic life.

The players in the beauty industry need to be mindful of the impact that their products are having on the marine ecosystem. Brands need to look at the entire life cycle of their products to assess the damage caused to the oceans. From the amount of water a product needs for manufacturing to the disposal of the plastic packaging, a whole host of issues need to consideration.

Blue beauty is not just a trend, and it's a movement. An informed decision that impacts your care positively and sustained in a manner should be at the core of your beauty care regime. Many brands now shy away from using materials in their products that cannot be recycled. Compostable lip balm tubes anyone?

- **How can I support the movement?**

You may ask what you can do as an individual to support the blue beauty concept. As the center of the beauty industry, you, the customer, are a significant part in taking this movement forward. First and foremost read up as much as you can about the concept. Decide to support brands that believe in the concept of Blue beauty. Be mindful of what product you need. You like the new lipstick or the face pack that has just come into the market. But do you need it? If not, avoid it. The blue beauty concept makes a deliberate attempt to start a discourse around the impact of their beauty choices not just on them but on the planet.

Blue beauty is a step towards restoring health and the color of the planet. Let's do our bit in turning the tide. The earth has enough for everyone's needs, but not everyone's greed.

Recent Innovation In The Beauty Tech Industry

From time immortal beauty and science have been the proverbial twin that shall never meet. Not anymore!

In a fiercely competitive market, beauty and skincare brands are forever looking into new domains of innovation. The latest trend in the beauty and skincare industry is beauty tech, which involves integrating the latest smart technology, ranging from Artificial Intelligence (AI) to Augmented Reality (AR), engaging the consumer and providing a more personalized experience than ever before.

In the past few years, big brands have started investing heavily in beauty tech. Beauty tech has now become a prominent display at the Consumer Electronics Show (CES)where several innovations are demoed and advertised. At CES, Smart Mirrors were the entire rave. These smart mirrors scan your skin for wrinkles, blemishes, fine lines, etc., and rate it accordingly from good to poor. Additionally, they also provide personalized tips and product recommendations based on these results.

More recently, custom-made foundation machines have been introduced, which promise exact matching foundation for your skin by using artificial intelligence to identify blemishes, spots, pimples, etc., and applying the perfect amount of foundation over them. Custom moisturizer based on skin condition and location-based weather and air pollution data is another fascinating innovation. Growing demand for personalized cosmetics has also led to the emergence of AR beauty apps that let you try makeup like lipstick or eyeshadow virtually, allowing the consumer to test a wide range before deciding what to buy.

Some brands, in addition to virtual makeup testing, also allow you to create custom products that are then 3D printed in stores! Another novelty in beauty tech is the 3D Face Mask printing system. A smartphone app scans and measures your facial features for a personally tailored face mask that not only fits perfectly but is also customized according to your skin condition and for different zones of the face like forehead, cheeks, or around the eyes.

Irrespective of the advantages of beauty tech, one major disadvantage of it is the luxury stuff that is way out of the reach of the general populace. The pricing seems affordable by only the rich, creamy society at present. However, with the passing time, as these technologies become more mainstream, they are expected to become more easily available and affordable to greater sections of society.

Hyper-Personalization And What It Represents.

The skincare industry is one of the most competitive markets. Every brand wants to be the best by selling their products and creating a niche for themselves. Most of the products that the skincare brands manufacture follow the techniques and ingredients from a set spectrum. Once a customer buys a brand, and it works for them, they tend to stick to it.

Hyper-personalization is much more than taking into account the type of your skin. It is the use of technology to provide specially curated products and services that suit your requirements. It is a client-centered approach that keeps them at the center of their services. Personalization of products for a customer is good: a simple idea, easy to implement; hyper-personalization is a debate. Once anything has hyper as the prefix, you have to be (at least) slightly wary of it.

The purpose of hyper-personalization is to make it easier for you to buy what you need. In many cases, experts even study your skin and suggest a product based on that. When you go to the store to buy a beauty product, you see different brands of the beauty product, and this makes it a difficult choice for you. Hyper-personalization helps you choose the best product out of a big pool to choose. It helps you have in your collection the skincare that works and makes you look good.

However, the problem with hyper-personalization (and this is what makes it hyper) is three-fold. First, the more personalized a product, the more issues it will face regarding manufacturing efficiency. The paradigm shift from mass production to customization had a huge impact on the items because instead of one big cake that everyone gets a share of. Each individual is given a different cake with varied ingredients and toppings. Secondly, it becomes difficult to cater to the customers' expectations after a point. Lastly, the more hyper-personalized a product, the more high-end and expensive it becomes, severely limiting the affordability of such products to a very large customer base.

Hyper- personalization takes you many steps closer to the look and feel you want and makes you stand out from the crowd. There is absolutely nothing wrong with buying a personalized product. When you're buying a skincare product it is best to seek the advice of experts. However, to hyper-personalize it to the extent of making a product only cater to an elite base of customers defeats the purpose of the skincare industry of reaching out to a broad-based audience.

The Future Of The Beauty Tech Industry

In a more distant future, we may be looking at technology that caters to skincare at a genetic level, custom hair care, skin analysis at your local drug stores, print at home makeup, and a lot more. Currently, major brands are involved in devising novel strategies in incorporating the latest available technologies to connect better with consumers and provide more personalized services and products. The aim is to create a thoroughly personalized and customized experience.

Soon, digital makeup trials, AR beauty apps, and 3D printed makeup may become industry standards, and users may even stop seeing these products as 'tech' but as part of their daily lives.

Turn Your Routine Into A Beauty Ritual.

Making your daily routine into a mindful ritual is turning a habitual act to a meaningful deed that can maximize the outcome and add value to our lives. Rituals that are repeated daily distinguish the time apart from other daily routines and let you pay undivided attention and focus to eventually open up a new possibility for better results.

Same goes for skincare and beauty. Your skincare routine can be a perfect time for mindful daily ritual and beauty meditation. Instead of rushing into your daily skincare routine or reluctantly doing it, viewing the whole series of skincare steps as a ritual will be the foundation of your best skin. Make it into a meditation session and be mindful of each touch you are giving yourself. Also it is a great time for beauty mantras.

You don't need to put in a lot of time and effort into it. Just 10 minutes morning and night will do. You are not taking the time out from any other schedule just for this. The skincare routine takes physical time and just the quality of the time is changing. You don't need to be at any specific place or need special props. You, your skin-friendly products and a few minutes is all you need.

Our lives are packed with schedules, to-do lists and chores that are never ending with limited time. Even sparing some time to take a break seems impossible and living mindful and taking the time out of our busy day seems almost impossible. When your skincare routine turns into a mindful ritual, we are one step closer to connecting with ourselves, living with senses and beauty based on our well-being. Have it simple and casual to be sustainable.

Pause for a moment and stay 'here and now' while you are in front of the mirror every day. Remember, your breath can be a great anchor to be at the present moment and be mindful. It makes you do it with deliberate intention and focus and even the slightest touch of your skin will deliver the care and effectiveness. Take time to observe and enjoy each and every feature of your skin and body which is the start of revealing your beauty. You are creating space for your beauty and the soft touch of circular and soothing motion gives you relaxation and comfort.

Not only the breathing itself helps by supplying fresh oxygen to the blood vessels and skin, calming your heart rate and relaxing the muscles it balances the autonomic nerve system. Skincare ritual will generally consist of these 3 acts: Cleansing, Moisturizing and Protecting. Each step will turn into a ritual that will reset, recharge, open and reflect on ourselves, reconnect to our deepest nature and reveal our wellbeauty.

Cleansing: Dirt, pollution, accumulated sun damage, the residue of skincare products, sunblocks and any harsh ingredients will be washed away. When it turns to a ritual, you are washing off the day's fatigue, free from the past and creating new space for a fresh new start.

Moisturizing: You are supporting and responding to your skin's needs by gently checking closely on how it feels, looks and supplying the moisture, nutrition and strengthening the skin barrier at the same time. Etc.

Protection: You are applying the needed ingredients and care that will guard the skin from sun, pollution, water loss and stress. When you focus on the act of protecting your skin, your intention will lead you to find more mindfulness in choosing the right products for you.

Skincare ritual is a perfect time for us to apply the RAIN process and recognize and allow our feelings and emotions you are going through and observe and let it go. It could be a time to let go of any tension and stress and come back to your peaceful senses. Your beauty ritual can go silently, or you can whisper the mantra to yourself. It doesn't always have to be a positive affirmation or blessings to yourself, it can just be the words to recognize and name your emotions at the moment. Just make it into the time you serve for your wellness purpose. Any instant or customized ritual can also act as the best solution for you.

If you find humming soothing and comforting while you are cleansing your face, saying "I am radiant" while brushing your hair, do follow whatever that serves your self-appreciation. If you prefer to light an aromatic candle or turn to soothing background music that will also add to raise the sense of ritual. Or the natural white noise or the bottles of your skincare products will be enough for you to get that feeling of ritual.

Important thing is that you set the skincare routine as a self-care ritual and practice respect for your skin and body as a part of you and it will bring you the best outcome you were looking for. It's the time I truly become the mindful manager of my beauty, and my beauty becomes my own standard. From applying a toner to spraying face mist on your face, putting on eye cream, taking a shower, changing your clothes, drawing eyeliner and even folding laundry and doing dishes, every single act of everyday life can turn into a beauty ritual and meditation of mindfulness. Mindfulness and meditation that will relieve the tension and the stress, the weight and burden of the day and turn your intention and awareness into your wellness will bring about the beauty benefits.

Beauty Routine Mediation- Caring For Your Neck.

Caring for your neck is very easy. Unfortunately, a lot of people do not pay attention to the neck as it is believed that too much care should not be given to the neck.

Interestingly, this is a simple example of beauty routine meditation.

You can find full, guided beauty meditation on our RESPEKT Beauty Meditation app.

Find a quiet place where you won't be disturbed for about 10 -15 minutes.

Remember the fact that your wellness will show on your skin.

- **Have your favorite moisturizer ready.**
- Find a comfortable seated position and settle in.
- Take a nice, slow and deep breath in and breathe out.
- Gently spread the moisturizer all over your neck and chest.
- slowly spread the moisturizer upward towards your face.
- Use gentle and soft motions to guide your thoughts.
- Allow your thoughts to come and go freely.
- Allow yourself to enjoy every second of this meditation.
- Close your eyes and enjoy the massaging until the moisturizer is fully absorbed.
- Open your eyes with a gentle smile.

PART FOUR

AGING BEAUTIFULLY

"Nature gives you the face you have at twenty;
it is up to you to merit the face you have
at fifty."
Coco Chanel

Whether 25 or 65, everyone wants to feel beautiful, and why shouldn't they? However, with the socially approved definition of beauty recognizing everything young, there is hardly any room for women who have entered menopause. Well, I have great news for you. Grab a teacup and drink to good health and beautiful skin!

"Grab a teacup and drink to good health and beautiful skin"

I am nearly in my fifties. I have to admit that discussing the age that has not yet been experienced starts from the fear that my looks and wellness in the future might not be attractive. But one thing is for sure that if I don't embrace my future self and appreciate it, who will do that for me? I do not want to have a very shallow perspective and let go of a precious part of my life. I want to cheer   myself up and discover my beauty so that I can be the steward and creator of it at every stage of my life.

The normal changes of getting older are inevitable. Even as you get older, there are some natural ways of maintaining your beauty as you get older. Fortunately, there are many skin rejuvenation products, facial products and numerous options available for women who are above the age of 50 and still desire to maintain a youthful appearance.

While you are younger, the type of lifestyle you favor can either leave a positive or negative effect on your skin. Some factors such as sun exposure, smoking, diet, and heredity play a huge role in affecting the way your skin looks when you are much older. Furthermore, stress and obesity can also affect your skin negatively considering that as you get older, your body is unable to produce new cells. It presupposes that your skin becomes less elastic and becomes prone to dryness. This same thing applies to your hair. It is why it is common to see women over 50 year with gray strands of hair. It is a product of the inability of the hair pigment cells to renew themselves.

Embracing your age doesn't mean you stop caring about it. Have you ever seen social media posts proclaiming that beauty doesn't last forever? Yes, the very same ones that have two photos juxtapose to each other. One is of a young woman with flawless skin and cascading mane and the other of an older woman with a face full of wrinkles. We have been socially conditioned to believe that beauty is all about youth that we cannot see the insecurities that this concept perpetuates.

Beauty Changes, Not Diminishes.

We can't mention it enough when discussing our beauty. It is a process in which beauty matures, deepens, subdivides and individualizes. Our eyes towards aging need to evolve.

I can say the story in this book so far is all about embracing and enjoying each stage of our life beautifully and age gracefully. Beauty is not limited to a certain range of age.

As I age, I know that my body will be more affected by the what the hormones in my body cast to it and I might face a face that I have never expected to be myself but that is what I need to embrace and care and cherish. The unexpected changes help me truly care for my emotional wellness and other areas of wellness while beauty meditation will help me truly appreciate my own beauty, the core of my being.

At this point of my life, what I regret the most is that I didn't really appreciate what I was born with. I took the beauty standards as true and tried to fit myself and that struggle has lasted so long. I was born with very dark hair, and I always envied lighter brownish hair and I never liked my dark eyebrows. I wanted something that I didn't have. I think that it is natural in some sense to want to be someone else and wanting what I don't have, and it can be a motivation to a fun change to enjoy new experiences and new self. But if it hinders me to not fully enjoy and appreciate what I have and who I am and push myself to meet the image that the world throws at me that hurts one's dignity and I will regret later. That was my case.

Now I've learned to like and love myself today more and more and I am looking forward to the future because with the practical practice of beauty meditation, I began to establish my philosophy of beauty and my awareness of my beauty grew strong.

You don't get prettier just by looking at the mirror. But saying nice things to yourself in the mirror will truly bring out the best in you. Reflecting yourself and cherishing yourself by beauty meditation is a sure way to be a more beautiful self.

Knowing oneself, own feelings and emotions, thoughts and own uniqueness enables you to reveal your beauty. Caring for your deepest emotions and stress is the act of self-care and skincare.

Embracing Aging: The Upside Of Getting Old

The desire to look young is so intense that some of us would go to any length to stay in time. Sagging skin, wrinkles, fine lines, crow's feet are signs not to be revered but feared. Beyond the regular wear and tear of age and the face that begins to lose its elasticity lie perks of aging. Not one or two but many. Growing old has its advantages that all of us experience but aren't consciously aware of.

Getting old is a good time to pursue your interest: Well, you may not have realized this before now, but getting older is an ideal time to try something new. You have worked so hard all your life that your interests and dreams took a back seat. Fortunately, as you get older, you can indulge in fulfilling all your desires.

Old age is a symbol of wisdom: You hear this all the time, but you may not have taken it seriously. The reality is that old age fills you with so much wisdom and experience and this is a wonderful feeling. It's because of this truckload of wisdom that you become the go-to person in times of any crisis or a tricky situation.

Confidence and comfort: When you were much younger, you found it difficult to be yourself because society expected you to behave in a certain way. It made it difficult for you to do what truly makes you happy because of high societal expectations. The good news is that getting older means that you get to live your life the exact way you please without seeking validation from anyone.

Tips To Help You Get Started.

As you get older, there are a few steps that you need to take to maintain your skin and look younger. They are:

Stop smoking: Smoking prematurely causes the skin to get older. So, if you smoke, stop smoking so that your skin can look younger.

Avoid sunbathing and tanning salons: Of course, you want to feel younger, so you feel sunbathing is the most considerable way to care for your skin. However, you are no longer in your twenties, so it is best to do what is best for your skin. Avoid staying too long in the sun from 10 am to 2 pm. It is because the sun's rays are at their peak at this period. If you must stay in the sun, please, wear a protective hat, sunglasses and a shirt covering your skin. Blotchy complexion and freckles are a result of excessive exposure to sun.

Wear sunscreen always: Use products that contain a percentage of zinc oxide and SPF 30 protection every day. Apply your sunscreen every two hours when you are outdoors. When your skin is damaged by the sun, it will result in wrinkles and an uneven skin tone.

Check your skin for signs of cancer: If you notice any unpleasant changes in your skin, please visit a doctor. Older and light-skinned people are always at risk of skin cancer. So, ensure you have a yearly check to play safe.

Proper meals and hydrate: Good meals are an effective way of repairing the skin and lots of water help you to stay hydrated at all times.

Make use of anti-aging products: As an older woman at the age of 50 or above, over-the-counter products can help to rejuvenate your skin. Pentapeptides are a chemical contained in beauty products that help the skin to produce collagen, which will give the skin a firmer look. Retinoid creams and prescription creams are also good options that will help the skin look beautiful even at an older age.

Make use of skin treatment: Getting old is a blessing and you must learn to appreciate this fact. A good way to appreciate your age as you get older is to use the right skin treatment to enhance your skin. One of the good ways of enhancing your skin is to make use of chemical peels. It removes fine lines and makes the skin around eyes and mouth smooth. On the other hand, wrinkles fillers are important for plumping up the skin and erasing lines. Microdermabrasion improves complexion, skin tone and color.

Mediation: I know that I had discussed meditation and its usefulness in the earlier part of this book. But I feel a great need to reiterate it, especially as it enhances the skin of older people. Meditation can help you significantly in living the holistic life that you deserve in your later years. Research has established many physical and psychological benefits of meditation that can help you lead a happy life as you age.

Meditation-A Way To Happier Senior Years

Our senior years are romanticized as being free of household responsibility and having time at hand to pursue the missed opportunities in life. These years are meant to live your dream. Unfortunately, growing old comes with its share of physical aches and pains, the empty nest syndrome, and unpredictable moods.

Meditation can help you significantly in living a holistic life that you deserve in your later years. Research has established many physical and psychological benefits of meditation that can help you lead a happy life as you age.

Read on to know how meditation benefits you in your later decades in life.

Meditation is all about awareness of the moment you live in. Awareness of every breath you draw and your surroundings. Meditation teaches you to slow down and let go.

Benefits Of Mediation For Older People

Slows down dementia: Meditation helps to slow down dementia that is most common with people above the age of 85 years. The capacity to remember is the foundation of how we function. From operating basic things like household appliances and driving a car to remembering where we live, memory governs everything. Losing one's memory may create havoc in your life. Meditation helps people feel more relaxed and less anxious by reducing cortisol, a stress hormone, which is associated with the increased risk of dementia. Meditation aids in increasing the thickness and gray matter. This in turn delays the aging process of your brain.

Helps you de-stress and increase focus: With so much going around us all the time, it's easy to feel overwhelmed. Anxiety and stress can severely compromise the quality of our life. Meditation makes you learn to be present at the moment and feel relaxed. Regular meditation helps your mind organize your thoughts better and have a clear perspective.

Sharpens mental alertness: Did you know that meditation invigorates your memory centers? I bet you didn't. Regular meditation leads to a change in the structure of your brain. The area associated with negative emotions like stress, anxiety, etc., diminishes and the area responsible for self-awareness expands.

Improves Your Sleep: People with poor sleeping habits often experience irritability and loss of focus. As you age, a good night's sleep becomes elusive and older people often complain of insomnia. Regular meditation is linked to the production of a higher level of melatonin, a hormone that regulates your sleeping pattern.

Makeup Trends For Mature Skin

All you have to do is take a good look around you to realize that something is missing in the beauty industry. From the advertisements that are made to the models that are used, youth sell! Whenever you talk of older people, all that makeup talks about is anti-aging! It's as if the only way makeup is used by the older generation is by hiding their age.

Wear your Wrinkles Proudly.

Society has told us that the appearance of wrinkles is the most frightening sign of being old. The mere glimpse of them makes one rush to buy an anti-wrinkle cream that promises eternal youth. If you are anywhere near 50 or above, wrinkles are a reality and can't stay hidden. Embrace your age, not hide it.

You may not be able to make your wrinkles vanish away, but you certainly can wear them tastefully. Using a foundation with a lightweight moisturizer would hydrate your skin and give it an even tone. Wrinkles, dark circles, and crow's feet make your eyes look dull. Focusing on the under-eye area and inner corners when you apply foundation will give shine back to your eyes.

Play Up Your Complexion

Everyone wants luminous skin that shines with the brilliance of the youth. However, with the appearance of wrinkles, the matt- finish that you use to look radiant may settle into the fine lines and between your wrinkles. The Korean beauty trend of "glass skin" that is taking the beauty industry by storm recommends having multiple hydrating products that sit lightly on the skin. It gives you clear, poreless skin no matter what your age is.

Be Bold with Your Lips

Bold lips are not the sole proprietor of the young! Scarlet lips look good on everyone. Break the myth of your senior years being the slave to dull and nude colors. Wear that bright red hue and face the world with confidence.

Go Natural with your Eyebrows.

Your later years in life are all about caring less and less about people, so why should your eyebrows care. It's about time that the makeup trends stop regulating your eyebrows. Sparse or bushy, let them be. No tweezers and no threading to achieve the so-called perfect uniform brows. All that needs is to apply a dark brown shadow and a tinted brow mascara throughout the eyebrows and you are good to go!

Blush Up

Rosy cheeks will rule. Blush has this universal appeal that caters to every age group. It looks especially fetching on mature skin. We suggest using a liquid blush to keep your skin hydrated, particularly if you have a dry skin type.

Makeup trends about mature skin are not about hiding your signs of aging anymore! The trends encourage loving your age and wearing it proudly.

Meditation For Aging Skin

It is a simple example of beauty meditation.

You can find full, guided beauty meditation on our RESPEKT Beauty Meditation app.

Find a quiet place where you won't be disturbed for about 5 minutes.

Remember the fact that your wellness will show on your skin.

- Begin with bringing your awareness to your breathing.

- Feel your mind clear, and breathe deeply.

- While breathing, focus on the thought that stress can affect your whole body and accelerate the aging process.

- It can break down the skin's collagen and elastin, form wrinkles and speed up sagging skin.

- Since stress is a part of life, what matters is how you handle it.

- Simply connect with your breathing, let your mind relax and let go of the past, let go of the past thoughts.

- Stress comes from worrying about the future, so take the time to sit at this moment and only think of what is going on right now.

- Think of only your breathing as you reduce your stress and improve your skin health.

- Mindful breathing while meditating adds oxygen to the skin, reserves energy, improves circulation, and relieves stress.

- This increased oxygen rejuvenates your skin and improves your complexion, reduces wrinkles, and slows down the aging process from the inside out. Making you look and feel younger.

- Breathe in and out deeply through your nose.

- And inhale again and exhale.

- Keep breathing as you think of only this moment, and you let stress slip from your mind and bring health to your skin.

Whenever you begin to feel stressed and aging, simply focus on your breathing while visualizing your skin, getting all the beauty benefits from it.

Embrace Aging

Not just the wrinkles, you would experience other signs of aging as well. The first step to feeling truly beautiful from within is to be comfortable in your skin.

Aging is a normal and inevitable process and no matter what products you use; your chronological age will eventually reflect on you. True comfort comes with truly accepting who you are. Stop fighting the ticking of the clock and embrace the signs of aging.

Breaking Stereotypes

Every year brings a new fashion trend with it. These trends try to slot you in watertight compartments based primarily on your age and appearance. Beauty more than trends, it is an expression of your individuality. By the time you are in your 50s, you know what works for you in terms of hair and makeup. Don't buckle under pressure to fit in with the crowd. You are not a crowd, you are you. Finally at 50 and beyond you have the confidence to be you. Follow the trend, break the trend, stick to your routine, or experiment with your looks: you can do what you want!

Anti-Aging?

Personally, when I hear the word antiaging, I wonder if there is a basic understanding of beauty. Now that the average span of a man's life has increased, the perspective of age should also change accordingly. Even though the word 'anti-aging' is rampant, let's not lose our aesthetic, attitude of life and self-love that knows how to savor the essence. I would like to call it "age care".

Just like the challenging for the future is never late at any stage of life, same goes for age care. Let everything ever done flow like a river and choose 'now' again to meet the happiest and most beautiful version of me. That is only possible with respect for oneself. This is the time to feel the beauty. We do not have much time to waste.. Let's use our time wisely.

Unlike other parts of our body, our skin is visible and works as a communicator. We are afraid of aging and falling behind and most of all that to show. It is always wise to be prepared and focus on prevention. This is the time to radiate.

Fortunately, either celebrities or people around us, we see so many figures that are aging beautifully. I get surprised at how beautiful and mature beauties are surrounding us. They are the whole package containing the days and stories that grew while deepening their own beauty which touches our heart and inspires us to be more beautiful people. Staying in the outdated concept of viewing aging as something to fight against loses its point.

How To Live Healthy At 50 And Beyond

At 50, you must have reached the zenith of your career, no mortgage or down payments are clawing at your back, your children are charting their own course. With everything taken care of you now have all the time to lavish attention to yourself.

For anyone who is 50 and above, your lifestyle needs a bit of tweaking so that you remain healthy and enjoy your life to the fullest.

Eat Well to Feel Well

What you eat gets reflected on your face and the overall functioning of your body. Healthy eating becomes the mainstay of a healthy mind and body for everyone above 50. Here are a few things that should become a part of your everyday food.

Rollback on Sodium: Sugar has become notorious for its adverse effects on health, but salt is no less! Our optimum sodium levels plummet as we age. At 50 and beyond, our sodium levels go down from 2,300 mg to 1,500 mg per day. High sodium can cause hypertension and blood pressure.

One of the most effective ways to cut down on salt is to severely limit your intake of processed food and rinsing canned food before consuming them. Another trick is to substitute salt with flavorful herbs while cooking.

High protein diet: Even though a protein-enriched diet is meant for all, it is highly recommended for anyone who is 60 and above. As you pass your 60th birthday, your muscles need a protein boost to strengthen them. Gorge on fish, lean meat, tofu, germinated black gram, lentils, and quinoa to give your body that much needed protein.

Go rainbow: A colorful platter is as good for your body as it is visually appealing. Loading up your plate with reds, greens, purples, whites, and oranges is your passport to good health in your senior years. The colorful fruits and veggies have antioxidants that fight aging. Fall in love with green- red and yellow bell peppers, green leafy vegetables, bright purple eggplant, red tomatoes and see the difference in the way you look and feel.

Add vitamin supplements: Adequate amounts of vitamins and minerals are needed for healthy aging. While it is recommended that you get your daily dose from an everyday diet, sometimes the diet isn't enough. There are a few vitamins that are specially meant for older men and women. Vitamin B12 helps strengthen your nervous system and blood cells. Vitamin D and calcium supplements are important for the robustness of your bones.

Don't Forget to Exercise

As opposed to the popular view, exercise is not just for kids and adults under 50, it has multifarious benefits for senior citizens as well. Physical activity has a strong connection with longevity. Exercise helps you keep your body in shape and substantially reduces age-related aches and pains.

Why should seniors exercise? Exercise comes with benefits for both body and mind. Daily exercise keeps your muscle, bones, and joints healthy, builds up stamina, keeps conditions like diabetes and arthritis under control. Not just the physical aspect, it is also an effective management technique.

How much exercise should one do at 50 and beyond? The ideal number of hours to be clocked in for a healthy adult is 150 minutes per week. The figure of 150 minutes may look daunting. However, all you have to do is divide your exercise time into manageable chunks of 10 minutes each three times a day. Exercise at this age is not synonymous with heavy duty workout. Brisk walking in the nearby park, flexibility exercises to keep the body agile will perfectly take care of your requirement.

Inculcate Healthy Habits

Habits make a man (and woman). Adopt habits that will keep your body in top condition.

Enough sleep: Don't underestimate the power of adequate sleep. A good night's sleep allows your body to rest and repair itself and you walk up restful and energetic. Poor sleeping habits on the other hand make you feel irritable and lethargic. Aim for 7-9 hours of sleep. Reducing disturbance, cutting down your screen time an hour before your bedtime, and using a low watt bulb will help you in getting good sleep.

Maintain oral hygiene: Oral hygiene becomes crucial as you age. The higher the oral health, the better the quality of elderly life. Tooth decay, dry mouth, gum diseases are commonplace among people who are 50+.

Annual medical checkups: Your risk of getting chronic illness including cancers increases once you reach your golden jubilee. Get into the habit of getting an annual full body check-up done. Be sure to include mammograms and colonoscopies.

Let your days of rest and relaxation be full of fun and enjoyment. Eating healthy, regular workouts, and adopting healthy habits will ensure that you look and feel the best in your senior years.

- *No more whispering- Bringing Menopause Visible*

Age inclusion has been the missing link of the discourse around the diversity of beauty and beauty products for a long time. Menopausal women form a significant percentage of the total American population. However, this group has largely been ignored with beauty conversations revolving solely around age-care products that will make you look at-least 5 years younger while shutting one's eyes to the reality of menopause.

Mature Aging: What Is It All About?

Like life and death, periods and menopause are inevitable. Unfortunate as it may sound, even though the period positive movement is gaining acceptance, a culture of silence still shrouds menopause. The appalling paucity of tools and products to assist women in navigating the choppy waters of menopause only leads to fueling of ignorance around it. While we have a plethora of beauty and skincare products and information to address issues from acne to dry skin and hair loss to postpartum conditions, one look around you will tell you that the market pertaining to mature aging products is negligible. The women under this demography are more or less invisible to the beauty industry.

The realization is slowly dawning on the beauty and skincare industry that the market is sadly bereft of the product line that specifically caters to the needs and requirements of the mature aging segment. Thankfully the market has understood that it's not just skincare products that are required but an integrated healing and beauty approach to make the effects of menopause manageable.

Menopause: Effects And How To Deal With Them

For most women, menopause is like an avalanche of physical changes that are difficult to cope with. From mood swings, night sweats and hot flashes to dry skin, frequent urination, weight gain and insomnia, it could be a very trying time for any woman.

In terms of skincare too, your body undergoes dramatic changes. It's always better to be prepared and know how to manage the effects than encountering them suddenly and not knowing what to do.

Dry skin: Oestrogen helps in maintaining the optimal level of moisture in our body. Menopausal causes a dip in the oestrogen level resulting in the consequent drop in the moisture content of the body thus causing dryness of the skin.

What can you do*:* There are steps that you can take to give the tender loving care that your skin requires during and after menopause.

- *Moisturize:* To keep your skin looking supple and plump, it is important to keep it hydrated and maintain the moisture level intact. Using a rich moisturizer with collagen, peptide, adenosine or any other age-care ingredients is the key to healthy skin during and post-menopause.

- *Exfoliation:* Your skin self-repairs itself creating a new layer every month. The process slows down with age leaving your skin looking dull and lifeless. It is recommended that you adopt a weekly exfoliation routine to bring back the glow. Exfoliation does away with the dead skin cells that accumulate on your skin unearthing the new layer and making it look fresh and dewy.

- *Sunscreen:* Sunscreen should be an essential part of your skincare no matter what your age is. A broad-spectrum sunscreen would not only act as a barrier between your skin and the harmful UV rays but also prevents the appearance of age spots.

Sagging skin: Menopause leads to the dipping of collagen level thereby making your skin lose its firmness and elasticity.

What can you do: You may consider using a skincare product that contains collagen to plump up your skin.

Hair Loss: Apart from your skin, another body part that takes a hit is your hair. Many women experience thinning hair or receding of the hairline with the onset of menopause.

What can you do: Set an appointment with a certified dermatologist to discuss steps for hair loss management.

A healthy lifestyle: Above all else, a healthy lifestyle will greatly help you in managing your menopause. Stress aggravates the symptoms. Hence keep away from stress as much as possible. Start meditation for a stress-free life. Meditation helps you relax and channelise your energy in a more effective manner. Mild exercising and a healthy diet also aid in negotiating the difficult road called menopause.

We need to make menopause visible in the beauty industry and we need to do it now because no one needs to go through it alone.

Take Care Of Your Skin.

Let's be real, being menopausal is far from being pretty. Hot flashes, weight gain, dry skin, frequent urination, and mood swings, it's excruciatingly exhausting. Your skin takes the beating when menopause strikes. With the dip in estrogen levels, your skin becomes dry, the plummeting collagen results in your skin losing the firmness and you may experience receding hairline due to menopausal induced hair loss. Just because we told you to embrace your age, doesn't mean you stop caring about it.

- Combat dryness of skin by applying a generous amount of moisturizer at least twice a day and even more if the dryness persists.

- Adopt weekly exfoliation that will gently clear your build-up of dirt, debris, and dead skin cells that slows down with age.

- Never forget your sunscreen. UV rays play havoc with your skin and make it dehydrated. Be it 25 or 70, always head out in the sun only after you have applied a broad-spectrum sunscreen.

- For regaining that tautness of your skin, use a skincare product with collagen as its key ingredient.

- To prevent hair loss, keep away from appliances and products that will make your hair brittle and fragile. Use products that are natural and gentle on your hair.

Adopt a Healthy Lifestyle

All the skincare will be in vain if your lifestyle isn't healthy. Stress is not only detrimental to your psychological health but to your appearance as well. External manifestations of menopause will only amplify with stress. Meditation, light exercise and healthy eating add quality to your life and help you navigate the tough terrain of menopause.

Aging like a fine wine doesn't mean you jump on the bandwagon of fashion trends that want you to look a certain way! It is all about celebrating the life you have led with panache. Don't let your age define the way you should look.

Skincare Trends For 50 And Above

For times immemorial, the concept of beauty had been all about youth. However, finally, the beauty industry is rethinking its definition of beauty and attractiveness. Thankfully this new definition is more inclusive of those 50 and over and is open to catering to their needs.

Looking attractive at 50 and beyond is not about hiding your age (which is a natural phenomenon, and inevitable). Rather, it is about celebrating who you are, carrying yourself with charisma, and as far as skincare is concerned, having healthy and radiant skin.

Keeping in tow with our evolving perceptions and paradigms about the concept of attractive skin, the skincare trends have also been changing. Here are the latest skincare trends that are in vogue nowadays:

Natural Ingredients

With age comes wisdom, and the demography above 50 is well aware and conscious regarding what they are putting on their skins. Products with natural ingredients like CBD oil, green tea extract, aloe vera, etc. antioxidants are trending like never before.

Minimalist Skincare Routines

Instead of buying a gazillion skincare products, many of which may not be very effective, veteran skincare enthusiasts are instead investing in lesser, but better products.

Hyaluronic acid

Hyaluronic acid has been making all the headlines in the skincare industry lately. And for good reason! It's a gooey, colorless substance that is naturally produced in the skin. It helps the skin retain its moisture, keeping it soft, smooth, and supple. It is also helpful in reducing redness, inflammation, and dermatitis.

Ceramides

Natural and nature-identical skincare products are in vogue today, and ceramides are another such product that are leading in the skincare market, especially for those 50 and above.

Ceramides are a kind of lipids that are found naturally in your skin. However, the quality, as well as quantity of ceramide production, declines with advancing age. Ceramides are the latest fad in the advanced aged generation so that they can replenish the ceramide levels in their skin.

Ceramides help maintain the structural integrity of your skin, holding the cells glued together and enhancing the physical barrier of your skin against external harmful elements like dirt or pollution. They also help seal the moisture in the skin. In a nutshell, ceramides promise hydrated, protected, and smoother skin.

Niacinamide

Niacinamide is another nature-identical product that is creating waves in the 50+ generation. Niacinamide is a form of vitamin B3 which is packed with a multitude of benefits. It increases blood circulation to your skin, it increases the production of ceramides, it helps against dark spots and hyperpigmentation, it protects your skin against external stressors, has anti-inflammatory properties, and it even plays a role in healing and regenerating the skin. Phew. What more do you want from a single ingredient?

Peptides

Incorporating peptides into your skincare routine provides you with immense benefits. Not only do they tell your body to boost up collagen production, they also protect you from the harmful UV rays of the sun. With peptides by your side, your skin radiates with youthful energy.

Collagen

It is thanks to collagen that your skin looks firm and supple. With age, collagen production decreases. Adding a collagen supplement to your already existing skincare routine would help you battle the signs of aging.

Vitamin C

Vitamin C is a powerhouse of antioxidants and aids in neutralizing free radicals that accelerate aging. It also enhances the production of collagen and significantly delays the appearance of the signs of aging.

Toners

Toning is a step that many miss out on in their daily skincare routines, and many may not even be aware of it. However, toners, which help balance the pH of your skin to its natural state, are the last step of cleansing used with cotton pads and the first step of moisturizing in everyday skincare routine. Toners are one of the upcoming trends in the 50+.

Healthy Lifestyle

50+ women know that caring for the skin is not just through the application of creams and serums. Fitness is in fashion, and so is eating healthy, wholesome food enriched with proteins, omega-3 fatty acids, vitamins, and antioxidants. What's out of fashion? Why, smoking and alcohol, of course.

Aging is a natural, inevitable process in the circle of life. However, being 50 does not mean that you cannot look beautiful and attractive. A few wrinkles do not mean that you cannot keep your skin looking lively and radiant at any age.

Beauty Quote Meditation "Beauty Is Power. Smile Is Its Sword."

This is a simple example of beauty quote meditation.

You can find full, guided beauty meditation on our RESPEKT Beauty Meditation app.

Find a quiet place where you won't be disturbed for about 5 minutes.

Remember the fact that your wellness will show on your skin.

- Try to feel as comfortable as possible.

- Gradually deepen your breath and focus on the following quote:

- Beauty is power; a smile is its sword.

- Think about beauty and what it means to you. What is true beauty in your eyes?

- Now think about a genuinely beautiful person. What makes them so attractive? Is it just physical? Or is it something more?

- Does intelligence make a person more beautiful? Good heart? Or the contributions to our society?

- Does their smile make them more beautiful?

- Relax your face and make sure you are not frowning.

- And then smile.

- When you smile you internalize that sensation of happiness, even if it doesn't feel completely sincere at the beginning. It's a simple feedback loop.

- A smile enhances your beauty, inside and out.

- And all those things make you a truly beautiful person.

"Beauty is power; and a smile is its sword."

EPILOGUE

"No one is you, and that is your superpower"
Dave Grohl

B eauty is personal. The only way to personalize your beauty is to own it for it is exclusively yours. To appreciate your beauty, you must respect it by making use of natural skincare products. Although there are many skincare products on the market, some of these products are harmful. Unfortunately, many beauty organizations in the skincare industry do not care about your skin rather they are only desirous of making money off you.

To protect and preserve your beauty, you must maintain healthy practices that are sustainable and beneficial to your skin health. Skincare practices are reserved for women as men also need to favor good skin care practices to nurture good skin. For women, age may also play a part in affecting how the skin looks. It is why when most women attain the age of menopause, they start feeling less beautiful because of societal conceptions about aging and the skin.

Interestingly, getting older is a good thing and comes with lots of benefits. To enjoy the benefits of aging, appreciate yourself at all times and stick to only good health practices and natural skin care tips. A good way to take care of your skin is to get a beauty philosophy that works for you. As for me, I stick to *"no chemicals, no stress."* In the same vein, our RESPEKT Beauty App provides information on maintaining your beauty and tip of your skin regardless of your skin type.

REFERENCES

Cohen, S., Kamarck, T., and Mermelstein, R. (1983). A global measure of perceived stress. Journal of Health and Social Behavior, 24, 386-396.

https://www.allure.com/gallery/best-celebrity-beauty-quotes

HBR (2013) The Ideal Praise-to-Criticism Ratio - Harvard Business Review. Hbr. https://hbr.org/2013/03/the-ideal-praise-to-criticism.

Obiora, Ntianu (2021) The Dark Side of social Media: How Unrealistic Standards are causing Identity Issues https://www.pulse.ng/lifestyle/beauty-health/the-dark-side-of-social-media-how-unrealistic-beauty-standards-are-causing-identity/hv4tffb

https://nysba.org/app/uploads/2020/04/Self-Assessment-Well-Being-Worksheet.pdf

SAMHSA SAMHSA Creating a Healthier Life: A Step-by-Step Guide to Wellness https://store.samhsa.gov/sites/default/files/d7/priv/sma16-4958.pdf

Jflowers Health Institute (2020) 8 Dimensions of Wellness https://jflowershealth.com/8-dimensions-of-wellness/

Yuen, Christal (2016) A Guide to Taking Care of Your Skin. Healthline. https://www.healthline.com/health/beauty-skin-care/skin-types-care#see-a-doctor

Wong, Michelle (2019)6 Anti-aging tips that'll transform your beauty routine. Healthline. https://www.healthline.com/health/beauty-skin-care/anti-aging-routine-skincare#-moisturizer

Jacoby, Sarah (2020) 11 Anti-aging skincare ingredients you should know. Self. https://www.self.com/story/antiaging-skin-care-ingredients

webMD (2021) Natural Beauty Tips for Women Over 50. webMD.https://www.webmd.com/beauty/women-over-50-natural-beauty-tips#1

Santos-Longhurst, Andrienne (2019) How to Live Your Best Life as you Age. Healthline https://www.healthline.com/health/aging-gracefully#tips

CPSIA information can be obtained
at www.ICGtesting.com
Printed in the USA
BVHW022153200222
629616BV00006B/318

9 780578 349916